HERITAGE STUDIES 6
ANCIENT CIVILIZATIONS
Fourth Edition

bju press®

Greenville, South Carolina

Note:
The fact that materials produced by other publishers may be referred to in this volume does not constitute an endorsement of the content or theological position of materials produced by such publishers. Any references and ancillary materials are listed as an aid to the student or the teacher and in an attempt to maintain the accepted academic standards of the publishing industry.

HERITAGE STUDIES 6: Ancient Civilizations Activity Manual
Fourth Edition

Writers
Carol Arrington Ardt, MEd
Jill Blackstock, MEd

Consultants
Dennis Bollinger, PhD
Dennae White, EdD

Biblical Worldview
Brian C. Collins, PhD
Bryan Smith, PhD

Academic Oversight
Jeff Heath, EdD

Editor
James Zemke, MA

Project Coordinator
Heather Chisholm

Designer
Michael Asire

Content Image Curator
James Frasier

Cover Illustration
Ben Schipper

Page Layout
Bonnijean Marley
Faith Mazunda
Carrie Walker

Illustrators
Vladimir Aleksic
Timothy Banks
Jonathan Bartlett
Zach Franzen
Josh Frederick
Del Thompson
Courtney Wise

Permissions
Sharon Belknap
Tatiana Bento
Sylvia Gass
Ashleigh Schieber

Photo credits appear on page 256.

© 2018 BJU Press
Greenville, South Carolina 29609
First Edition © 1998 BJU Press
Second Edition © 2000 BJU Press
Third Edition © 2012 BJU Press

ISBN 978-1-62856-229-3

15 14 13 12 11 10 9 8 7 6 5 4 3 2 1

CONTENTS

The Study of History

Lacy

Fill in the blanks to complete the outline.

I. How do __Historians__ know what happened in the past? (page 4)

  A. Historians often look for __evidence__ about earlier __events__.

  B. They look for clues that can be dug out of the __ground__.

II. There is a __written__ record for how _____ began. (page 4)

  A. The Bible is the only completely reliable __source__ that reveals how __the world__ began.

  B. In Genesis 1:1, __it is recorded__ recorded, "In the beginning God __created__."

Moses was the Hebrew lawgiver and prophet of God.

III. The Bible is the Word of __God__ in addition to being a __written__ record. (page 4)

  A. Moses wrote __exactly__ what God __told__ him to write.

  B. Moses was able to __accuretly__ record God's Word because it was given by __Gods inspiration__

IV. The period when __humans__ supposedly evolved is called __pre history__. (page 5)

  A. There is no prehistory in the __Biblical__ sense because the Bible contains the record of the __history__ of the world.

  B. In Genesis, Moses records the __eye witness__ testimony of the __devine__ eyewitness, God.

  C. People were __directly__ created by God about 6,000 or __7,000__ years ago.

The Study of Ancient History

Fill in the blanks to complete the outline.

I. Why study ancient history? (page 6)

    A. People receive the _____ of a good story that is based on _____.

    B. People can use true stories of the past to know how to live in the _____ and the _____.

    C. History teaches people about _____.

    D. The study of history provides people an _____ to _____ God.

II. How do people study history? (page 6)

    A. The historian studies _____, physical man-made _____ from the past.

    B. The historian uses _____, the passing of information from generation to _____.

    C. A historian uses written records that are _____ sources, or firsthand accounts.

    D. A historian may use _____ sources such as an encyclopedia entry, _____, or a review of art or literature.

Cuneiform tablet from Ebla dating to ca. 3000 BC

III. A historian needs to evaluate the _____ of artifacts, traditions, and written records. (page 7)

    A. Some historical _____ may present only _____ side of the story.

    B. How a historian interprets evidence results from his _____.

    C. A Christian historian will _____ evidence from a worldview based on the _____.

    D. A historian needs to understand what is _____ and what is _____.

    E. A Christian historian remembers that God _____ and _____ all things, including history.

Creation, Fall, Redemption

_____

Fill in the blanks to complete the outline.

    I. God created the world and everything in it. (page 9)

      A. God created the world by _____ it into existence.

      B. God created _____ in His own _____.

    II. God created _____ with a purpose. (page 9)

      A. Genesis 1:28 records God's purpose for people in the _____.

      B. God's command calls humans to _____, subdue, and have _____ over the earth.

      C. God placed the first man and woman in a garden with _____ that would take them into a wider _____.

   III. God provided the _____ people would need to advance human _____. (page 9)

      A. When people work together in civilization, _____ results.

      B. God gives people power to exercise some _____ over nature and to _____ communities of people.

   IV. The Fall resulted when Adam and Eve _____ God's _____. (page 10)

      A. Adam and Eve wanted to become like _____, and they chose to _____ God's law.

      B. Adam and Eve did _____ become like God; instead their _____ brought sin, suffering, and _____ into the world.

   V. For a _____ to flourish there must be a form of justice. (page 10)

      A. People are expected to do _____ and _____ the rights of others.

      B. Governments ensure _____ by punishing evildoers.

      C. God carried out justice by _____ Adam and Eve from the _____.

continued on next page

Creation, Fall, Redemption

_____

Fill in the blanks to complete the outline.

VI. For a civilization to prosper, people need to share the same _____ to work
_____. (page 10)

   A. People have _____ within a social structure.

   B. Problems result when _____ do not do right and do not respect the
_____ of others.

VII. There were consequences of the Fall. (page 10)

   A. The earth rebelled against people's efforts to _____ it.

   B. People turned away from _____ and worshiping the one true God.

VIII. The Bible reveals a special kind of history, the history of _____. (pages 10–11)

   A. Genesis 3:15 promises that God will provide _____ through Jesus Christ.

   B. God is working to restore His people to bear God's _____ as He intended it to be.

   C. One day Jesus will return in power to rule over the entire earth with _____ and
_____.

   D. God will change the _____ so thorns and thistles will no longer affect the
_____.

   E. God's _____ plan to build a just and righteous civilization will be fulfilled in the
new _____.

One day, God will restore the earth.

Geography and the Earliest Civilizations _____

Fill in the blanks to complete the outline.

I. The Bible provides clues about the _____ of the pre-Flood world. (page 12)

  A. The garden in which God placed the first people was part of the region called Eden.

  B. The river that flowed out of _____ and into the garden divided into four rivers that flowed to _____ parts of the world.

  C. The _____ and Euphrates Rivers that exist today are _____ the same that flowed out of Eden.

II. The universal _____ made massive _____ in the earth's geography. (page 13)

  A. The force of _____ was powerful enough to carve the _____.

  B. The Flood may have moved the _____ of the earth.

  C. Scientists who believe in Creation note that the earth's _____ could have been split during the Flood, causing the _____ to move.

Grand Canyon National Park at sunrise

III. The _____ geography of the earth changed after the Flood. (page 13–14)

  A. After Noah and his family left the _____, God told them to refill the earth with _____.

  B. Genesis 10, called the _____, details where the _____ of Ham, Shem, and Japheth relocated.

  C. The descendants of Noah's sons gathered in the plain of _____ to build a city and a tower to prevent being _____ in the earth.

  D. God caused the people of _____ to speak _____ languages so that they could not work together.

  E. People formed groups that spoke the same _____, and these groups scattered _____ the _____.

The First Civilization: Cain's City

_____

Fill in the blanks to complete the outline.

I. Cities are central locations for _____, _____, and culture. (page 15)

   A. The first chapters of _____ show the characteristics of the first city, Enoch.

   B. Genesis 10:10 describes Nimrod as having a _____, showing that a _____ was an early form of government.

II. People are often _____ into social classes, with each social class having a different _____.

   A. When the Bible describes early people, it gives information only about the _____ they held.

   B. It is _____ to assume that the jobs early people held put them into _____.

III. Job _____ occurs when a person devotes his time and talent to a specific type of work that becomes his _____. (page 18)

   A. Early humans were not solely dependent on _____ and _____, as evolutionists believe.

   B. People were able to grow _____ food than they needed, allowing some people to use their time and _____ in areas other than farming.

IV. People communicate through _____, music, and written language, and they use science to develop _____ to learn about their world. (pages 15, 18)

   A. The Bible indicates that people used technology to do different _____ and build _____.

   B. Genesis 4:22 describes _____ as a _____ of bronze and iron.

   C. Genesis 4:21 describes _____ as the father of those who played the _____ and pipe.

   D. Adam was the first human to write a _____, and _____ put his boast into poetry.

V. Religion is a system of basic values, beliefs, and behaviors directed in _____ to God and _____ in community with other people. (pages 15, 19)

   A. Adam and Eve and their descendants had _____, even though they did not have the _____.

   B. Because people have _____ natures, sin _____ the practice of true religion.

   C. False _____ form when people reject God and His _____.

Studying History

Mark all the correct answers.

1. It is important to study ancient history because

   ○ it provides an opportunity to praise God.
   ○ history teaches people about themselves.
   ○ written records are more important than artifacts.

2. Sources that a historian uses to find out about the past are

   ○ artifacts.
   ○ tradition.
   ○ written records.

3. A Christian historian believes that

   ○ early humans were primitive ape-like creatures.
   ○ man has always been intelligent.
   ○ God knows and controls all things.

Ancient religious symbol

Number the steps in order to show how a historian produces a historical account.

_____ He compares the sources and chooses the most reliable ones.

_____ He gathers primary written sources about his subject.

_____ He combines information from several sources.

_____ He evaluates the sources for strengths and weaknesses.

_____ He interprets and explains why an event happened and how it remains important.

_____ He presents the completed historical account for others to study and evaluate.

_____ He produces a narrative that represents the majority of his research.

Answer the questions.

11. What is tradition? _____

_____

_____

12. What are primary and secondary sources? _____

_____

_____

13. What sometimes causes historians to disagree over how to interpret evidence? _____

_____

_____

14. What does a Christian's worldview begin with? _____

_____

_____

Evaluating Historical Resources

_____

Examine each source. Complete the chart to determine whether each source is primary or secondary.

Source title		
Author		
Was it written at the time of the event or later?		
Form of information (letter, speech, textbook, encyclopedia)		
Primary or secondary source		

Determine the author's viewpoint. Record your answers in the chart with examples from the source.

Source title		
What is the main idea?		
Does the author use Scripture or biblical truth?		
Does the author use language that shows emotion or opinion? (Look for words such as _think, feel, best, worst, might,_ or _should._)		
Does the author provide only one viewpoint or both sides of the event?		
Does the author use factual statements? (These statements usually answer _who, what, when,_ and _where_ questions.)		

Study Guide

_____

Define the terms.

1. prehistory_____

   _____

2. worldview_____

   _____

Complete the section.

3. What does the Bible teach about inspiration? _____

   _____

   _____

4. What makes the Bible a reliable source for the origin of humans? _____

   _____

   _____

List three reasons for studying ancient history.

5–7. _____

   _____

   _____

Write _True_ if the statement is true. If the statement is false, write the correction for the underlined words.

_____ 8. <u>Moses</u> recorded God's historical account of the beginning of mankind in Genesis 1:1.

_____ 9. God provides a <u>historical</u> account of what happened on the first seven days of Creation.

_____ 10. The Bible records that <u>Daniel</u> was a man who strove for power and resisted God.

_____ 11. A historian compares written records, then chooses the most <u>interesting</u> sources.

_____ 12. Some historians believe that early humans were primitive, <u>ape-like</u> creatures.

_____ 13. People were created by God <u>millions of</u> years ago.

Study Guide _____

Complete the charts.

14. Write what the Bible says about the beginning of history and what evolutionists believe about prehistory.

Topic	Biblical beginning of history	Evolutionary prehistory
Beginning of people		
Speech and written language		
Agriculture and cities		

15. Identify three types of sources that a historian uses and give an example of each. Include examples of primary and secondary sources.

Source	Example

Complete the section.

16. What should a historian keep in mind as he evaluates historical sources in regard to their viewpoints, their strengths, and their weaknesses to form a historical account? Include in your answer how a Christian historian looks at sources.

_____

_____

_____

_____

_____

_____

_____

_____

Essay Questions

Match the definition with the correct term.

_____ 1. evaluate

_____ 2. trace

_____ 3. analyze

_____ 4. justify

_____ 5. classify

_____ 6. compare and contrast

_____ 7. predict

_____ 8. interpret

A examine critically to identify causes, key factors, possible results, and relationships

B follow the development or steps of something in chronological order

C give the meaning or importance of

D judge something's significance or importance using evidence as support

E show how things are similar and different

F sort into groups based on shared characteristics

G support a position with specific facts and reasons

H tell what will happen in the future based on an understanding of the past

Plan the essay on a sheet of paper. Then write it below.

9. Analyze the importance of studying ancient history.

_____

_____

_____

_____

_____

_____

_____

_____

_____

_____

_____

Essay-Writing Steps	
1. Read the question.	6. Write the main points with supporting facts and details.
2. Underline key words.	7. Write a closing statement.
3. Plan the response.	8. Evaluate the essay.
4. Order the main points.	
5. Write an opening statement.	

Examining an Artifact

Examine and record your observations about both sides of the coin.

	Observations
Material made of	
Languages	
Words	
Numbers	
Buildings	
People	
Dress	
Religion	
Other observations	

Draw conclusions using your observations. Be ready to explain your answers.

1. List four things archaeologists might conclude from the coin about an unknown civilization.

   _____

   _____

   _____

   _____

2. What kinds of sources might have been in the excavation that would help test their guesses about the coin?

   _____

   _____

   _____

   _____

List ten items from your house that could be used by a future archaeologist to determine something about you.

3. _____   8. _____

4. _____   9. _____

5. _____   10. _____

6. _____   11. _____

7. _____   12. _____

Creation, Fall, Redemption

Answer the questions.

1. In what ways are humans created in God's own image? _____

   _____

2. What is the Creation Mandate? _____

   _____

3. How did the Fall change the unfolding of human history? _____

   _____

   _____

   _____

   _____

4. What does Genesis 3:15 reveal about God's history of redemption? _____

   _____

   _____

Write the correct name of each theme of civilization. Write the correct words to complete the meaning of each theme.

5. _____ is the idea that people should do right and respect the rights of others.

   _____ are obligated to ensure _____ by _____ people

   to do _____ and by punishing _____.

6. _____ is the ability to bring things under control. For civilizations, it includes the

   ability to command _____ of people and to exercise some _____

   over _____. The biblical _____ in Genesis 1:28 to exercise

   _____ over the earth implies a _____ use of power.

7. _____ is a status that people have within a society that gives them certain rights, privi-

   leges, and duties. Citizenship gives people the _____ to _____ their

   civilization, but it also imposes _____ that call them to be _____. Bib-

   lically, a Christian's view of citizenship should be shaped by the knowledge that _____ are

   made in the _____ of God and that they are called to have _____ over

   the earth.

8. _____ is the physical geography in which civilizations are located. God made people to

   live on the earth and to _____ over the world by _____ the environ-

   ment to meet _____ needs. Knowing how people have _____ and

   _____ their environment is essential to the study of world _____.

The Pre-Flood World

_____

Answer the question.

1. Why is it impossible to find the exact location of Eden on a map of the world today? _____

_____

_____

_____

_____

_____

Complete the section.

2. Illustrate and label the possible geography of the pre-Flood world as described on Student Text page 12.

Features of Cain's Civilization

_____

Write the name of each feature of a civilization. Write words to complete the meaning of each feature.

1. _____ Cities are central locations for government, religion, and culture. A government manages _____ and provides _____, an _____, and _____ of conduct.

2. _____ People are often divided into social classes. Each class, or level, of people has a different _____.

3. _____ Each person focuses on a specific job or trade. They then rely on _____ with other people to supply _____ and _____ to meet their other _____.

4. _____ As people work together in a civilization, they communicate through art, music, and written language. They also use _____ to develop _____ and to learn about their _____.

5. _____ Religion is a system of basic values, beliefs, and behaviors that are directed in worship toward God and lived out in community with other people. False religion _____ that which is not _____, and this idolatry corrupts _____, _____, and _____.

Write details about each subject in the table.

Pre-Flood and early post-Flood eras	
Arts	
Sciences	
Job specialization	

Complete the section.

6. How did world religions degenerate from the original belief in the one true God?

_____

_____

_____

_____

Study Guide

_____

Answer the questions.

1. Why are people able to think, love, use language, know right and wrong, and enjoy relationships as God can?

   _____

   _____

2. What record states God's purpose for creating people, and what is God's purpose for mankind?

   _____

   _____

3. In what ways did the Fall affect the development of history? _____

   _____

4. What does Genesis 3:15 reveal will happen in human history? _____

   _____

Write _True_ if the statement is true. If the statement is false, write the correction for the underlined words.

_____ 5. The universal flood made <u>minimal</u> changes to the earth's geography.

_____ 6. The Flood may have moved the <u>continents</u> of the earth.

_____ 7. The continents on either side of the <u>Pacific Ocean</u> seem as though they could fit together.

_____ 8. The <u>plates</u> that make up the earth's crust still continue to show some movement.

_____ 9. Scientists who believe in <u>evolution</u> note that the continental plates could have been split during the Flood.

Complete the map.

10. Refer to Student Text page 14 to color each box in the map key a different color. Match the colors from the key to color areas on the map where each of Noah's sons migrated. Label the Mediterranean Sea.

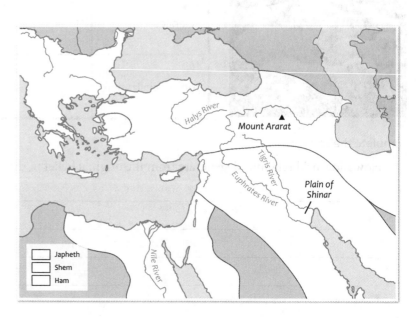

Study Guide

Complete the section.

11. Why would people have formed cities both before and after the Flood?

_____

_____

_____

12. Give examples of the arts and sciences that arose in the pre-Flood and the post-Flood eras.

_____

_____

_____

13. What job specializations were needed in order to use the natural resources of copper and tin at this time?

_____

_____

14. What other job specializations probably existed at that time?

_____

_____

Mark all the correct answers.

15. World religions degenerated from the original belief in one God because ___.

- ○ all people knew about the true God from the beginning, but they rebelled against God and stopped worshiping Him
- ○ people developed religious myths that were similar to the truth
- ○ people corrupted the truth that they knew

Match each term with its definition.

_____ 16. A group of people who establish cities, governments, social classes, specialized jobs, arts, science, written language, and religion

_____ 17. A son of Noah; received a curse for his wickedness; his descendants founded nations in the Far East, Africa, and along the eastern coast of the Mediterranean Sea

_____ 18. A flood in which water covers the entire earth; often used to refer to the flood of Noah's time

_____ 19. A system of customs including language, religion, government, economy, and arts that groups of people use to develop their world

_____ 20. Christ's act of rescuing and freeing people from sin; salvation

_____ 21. Man whom God saved from the Flood with his wife, three sons, and his sons' wives; directed by God to build an ark and put every kind of animal in it

A	redemption
B	universal flood
C	Noah
D	civilization
E	Ham
F	culture

Mesopotamia

Complete the facts about each topic.

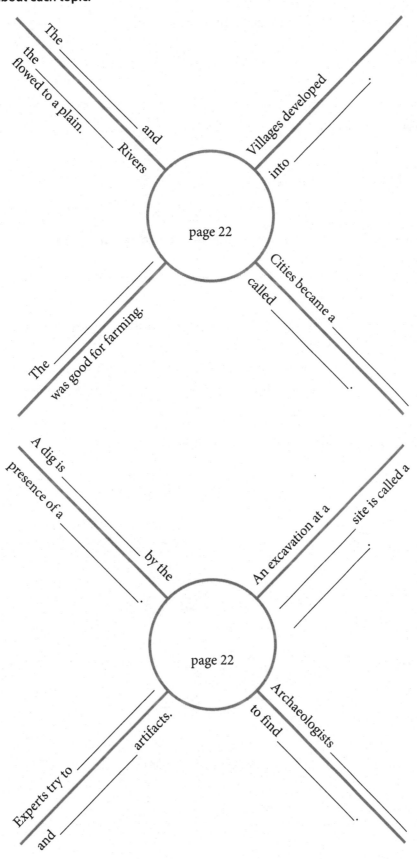

The _____ and
the _____ Rivers
flowed to a plain.

Villages developed
into _____.

The _____
was good for farming.

Cities became a
_____
called _____.

page 22

A dig is _____
presence of a
_____ by the
_____.

An excavation at a
_____ site is called a
_____.

Experts try to _____
and _____ artifacts.

Archaeologists _____
to find _____.

page 22

Sumerian Civilization

Answer the questions.

1. Why were civilizations able to flourish in the Fertile Crescent? _____

    _____

2. How did Sumer develop? _____

    _____

3. What is the role of an archaeologist? _____

    _____

4. What do archaeologists do with an artifact once it is found? _____

    _____

Write *True* if the statement is true. If the statement is false, write the correction for the underlined words.

_____ 5. An archaeologist digs <u>quickly</u> to avoid damaging fragile objects.

_____ 6. Leonard Woolley was an archaeologist and expert in <u>Mesopotamian</u> studies.

_____ 7. Archaeological evidence shows that Sumer was one of the <u>earliest</u> civilizations after the Flood.

_____ 8. Artifacts reveal the biblical city of Ur was a <u>small</u> place.

_____ 9. Woolley's excavation of a cemetery in Ur contributed to understanding the <u>Sumerians</u>.

Write the name of the location next to each corresponding number.

10. _____

11. _____

12. _____

13. _____

14. _____

15. _____

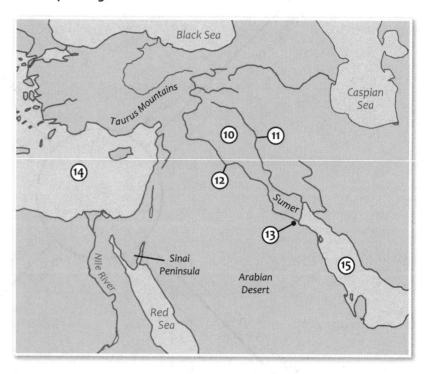

Color the Fertile Crescent on the map.

Mesopotamia

_____

Complete the details for each topic.

Topic	Details
Farming pages 24–26	Early _____ were pieces of wood that made long, shallow _____ in the _____. Eventually, farmers found that hitching _____ to a _____ with a _____ helped prepare even more land for _____. Farmers were the _____ known people to use the _____. Akkadian cylinder seal showing a man leading an ox as it pulls a seeder plow guided by other men, 2340–2180 BC
Flood Control pages 24–26	Sumerians built _____ of dirt to hold back _____, protecting their homes and _____.
Irrigation pages 24–26	A farmer could use _____ to keep his crops _____ throughout the dry _____. Sumerians built _____ _____ to hold _____ supplies. They dug _____ to carry water from the _____. Irrigation provided water for _____ and _____.
City-States pages 24–26	_____ people needed to farm because farmers produced a _____ of food. People worked at _____ jobs and trades that helped create and maintain the _____. _____ _____ grew into villages, and villages grew into _____. Each Sumerian city developed into a _____. A city-state was _____ of other city-states. It was usually ruled by a _____ who represented the _____. City-states formed strong _____ because of battles with other city-states for _____ and _____. A powerful city-state named _____ existed during the lifetime of _____.

Mesopotamia

Complete the details for each topic.

Topic	Details
Society pages 27–29	There were _____ social classes in the Sumerian civilization. The _____ _____ included people that had the most _____. People in this class included _____ _____, _____ _____, and _____. The largest class was the _____ _____. It included farmers, _____, merchants, _____, and _____ _____. People who were _____ made up the lowest class. Even though they were under the rule of their _____, they had certain _____.
Fishermen, Merchants, and Traders pages 27–29	Fishermen returned home from the river to sell their _____ at the _____ _____. Business was conducted by _____, _____, _____, and _____ on the docks of the _____ _____. Early trade was done by _____. Business dealings were recorded on soft clay _____ by _____ using a reed _____. After each sale was _____, it was wrapped in a clay _____ and stored in the _____. When two _____ finished a _____ deal and the scribe put his last _____ on the tablet, each man had to sign it using a _____ seal. Sumerian property deed from 3000 BC recorded with pictographs
Artisans and Buyers pages 27–29	Imported _____ were brought from the docks to the city of Ur and delivered to _____ who made them into _____ for _____ or goods for _____ to buy. Some of the busiest artisans shops sold _____ made of _____ or wool thread. Clay was a _____ material used to make _____ on a _____ _____. A special craft in Ur was _____ _____ made from _____ _____ from the river. The artisan sometimes surrounded the design with a bright _____ _____ called _____ _____.

Study Guide

_____

Match each term with its definition.

_____ 1. silt

_____ 2. Ur

_____ 3. irrigation

_____ 4. Mesopotamia

_____ 5. Sumer

_____ 6. barter

_____ 7. tell

> **A** a mound made up of layered dirt and the remains of buildings
> **B** a sediment of very fine particles containing rock and minerals that is found in the bottom of bodies of water
> **C** a system in which people exchange goods and services for other goods or services
> **D** the ancient region between the Euphrates River and the Tigris River
> **E** a way of supplying water to land or crops
> **F** a powerful city-state in Sumer
> **G** one of the first civilizations in Mesopotamia

Complete the section.

8. Who was the archaeologist who uncovered artifacts from Ur and the land of Sumer? _____

_____

9. What experts are needed for an archaeological dig? _____

_____

_____

10. What advances were made in farming, and how did they make the work of the farmer easier? _____

_____

_____

_____

_____

11. How did Sumer develop from farming settlements to city-states with a more centralized government?

_____

_____

_____

_____

12. What was the importance of trade in Sumer? _____

_____

_____

_____

_____

Study Guide

13. What is an example of how archaeology supports the Old Testament? _____

_____

_____

_____

_____

Mark all the correct answers.

14. The role of an archaeologist includes

    ○ locating an archaeological site and drawing a map for the dig.
    ○ photographing, labeling, and recording objects found at a dig.
    ○ studying artifacts to find clues about people from the past.

15. The Fertile Crescent was a good place for a civilization to flourish because

    ○ of its location between the Persian Gulf and the Mediterranean Sea.
    ○ the land was good for farming.
    ○ it was where Shem's descendants migrated.

16. The scribe and his tools are important because

    ○ he carefully recorded business transactions using a stylus in soft clay.
    ○ he put the clay tablets in clay envelopes.
    ○ archaeologists learn about Sumerian economics from the scribe's careful records.

17. Two merchants finished a business deal

    ○ using the scribe's stylus to sign their names in the soft clay.
    ○ after the scribe put his last marks on the tablet.
    ○ by each rolling a cylinder seal across the wet clay tablet.

18. Artisans in Ur used raw materials to

    ○ make products that buyers purchased for everyday use, such as cloth and pottery.
    ○ make beautiful objects, such as jewelry and fine dishes, to be sold in Ur or shipped to other cities and lands.
    ○ make a special craft called shell inlay.

19. Sumerian social classes included

    ○ slaves, who were the lowest class.
    ○ city-state rulers, governmental officials, and priests that made up the upper class.
    ○ farmers, fishermen, merchants, traders, and skilled workers that made up the middle class.

Mesopotamia

Complete the details about each topic.

Topic	Details
School and Family pages 30–33	Sumerian schools, called _____-houses, were attached to the _____. Students were usually _____ from _____ families. The boys received _____ that helped them become _____. _____ taught their children _____ and _____. Men were at the _____ of their _____. _____ and women born of _____ were allowed to learn to _____ and _____. Some women held _____ positions. Women conducted _____ and owned _____.
Clothing pages 30–33	Sumerians made _____ from wool or flax. Men wore _____ garments or robes _____ at the _____ shoulder. Women pinned their _____ at the _____ shoulder. Both men and women wore _____, including _____, necklaces, and _____.
Priests and Religious Beliefs pages 34–35	The _____ religion rejected the one _____ God. The people practiced _____. A temple called a _____ stood in the _____ of Ur. The ziggurat at Ur was orignally built by a _____ named _____. He built the temple to _____ the _____ god. Mesopotamians worshiped _____ of gods. One god that people worshiped in Ur was the moon god _____. Priests and _____ sacrificed _____ and followed _____, believing this devotion would keep the gods _____. The people were taught that only priests could _____ directly with the gods. This made priests _____ in Mesopotamia.
Kings and Government pages 34–35	At first, the _____ chose a _____ leader to defend the city-state in _____ against other city-states. When the _____ was over, the military _____ was expected to return to _____. Some of these leaders held on to their _____ and became _____. This was the beginning of _____. Eventually, every _____ had its own _____. Sumerians believed that a _____ selected the king, giving him _____. The priest acknowledged the king as the god's _____ to _____ the city-state. The _____ was the center of _____ as well as the _____ of Sumerian _____. Each king served as _____ _____ and _____.

Compare and Contrast

Write each statement in the correct column to complete the chart.

The gods complain about fulfilling their duties.

Work is a blessing.

The people create gods in their own image.

People are created in the image of the one true God.

God is perfect.

There are many gods.

There is one true God.

People show they are made in God's image when they work and rule over the earth.

The gods are not morally perfect.

✳ Mesopotamian Religious Beliefs	✝ Biblical Truth

Study Guide

Write *True* if the statement is true. If the statement is false, write the correction for the underlined words.

_____ 1. Leonard Woolley discovered a wooden box that he called the <u>Standard of Ur</u>.

_____ 2. The Sumerian schools were known as <u>tablet-houses</u>.

_____ 3. Boys received instruction that helped them become <u>farmers</u>.

_____ 4. Parents in Sumer taught their children <u>obedience</u> and respect.

_____ 5. In Sumer, <u>women</u> were the heads of their families.

_____ 6. Women were allowed to conduct <u>business</u> and own property.

_____ 7. Only the <u>priests</u> could communicate directly with the gods, making them powerful in Mesopotamia.

Complete the section.

8. What is a ziggurat? _____

9. What is the worship of many gods called? _____

Write an essay below.

10. Contrast Mesopotamian religious beliefs with biblical truth. Include at least three beliefs.

_____

_____

_____

_____

_____

Mark all the correct answers.

11. What contributed to the need for a well-organized government to manage resources?

   ○ When Mesopotamians began to live in cities, a large portion of the population stopped growing its own food.

   ○ People who farmed needed to grow enough food to trade with those who did not farm.

   ○ A manager was needed to see that surplus food was made available to everyone.

12. What events led to the beginning of kings?

   ○ City-states in Sumer needed more farmers to farm more land.

   ○ The priest of the city-states tried to pick the best military leader to defend that city-state in battle.

   ○ After the fighting was over, some leaders remained in power instead of returning to normal life.

13. What was true of government in Sumer?

   ○ The king was considered to be a god's highest representative on earth.

   ○ The temple was the seat of the Sumerian government.

   ○ Each king was the chief lawmaker and judge.

Mesopotamia

_____

Complete the details about each topic.

Topic	Details
Writing pages 36–37	Sumerians used a _____-shaped writing known as _____. Some people carved cuneiform onto a _____ to make a _____.
Math, Science, and Technology pages 36–37	People of Mesopotamia were the first to recognize the concept of _____ and to give a number a place value. They developed a number _____ based on the number _____. They used _____ to measure _____ and build _____. A system of _____ weights was created for business _____. Mesopotamians used the cycles of the _____ to develop a _____-month _____, and they divided the year into two seasons: _____ and _____. They developed the _____ plow, as well as systems for water _____ and _____. The invention of the _____ improved _____, and the _____ improved boat travel. They advanced medicine by coming up with a _____ and a _____ for symptoms.
Music pages 38–39	Musicians played _____, tambourines, reed _____, and _____ instruments called _____. Music was important to _____ rituals and daily _____.
Literature pages 38–39	Sumerians recorded stories, proverbs, and _____. A well-known _____ poem is the _____. This poem relates a story of a great _____ and describes how Utnapishtim built a _____ and gathered aboard his _____. Civilizations developed their own _____, creating different _____ of a great flood.
Arts pages 38–39	Mesopotamians made jewelry of _____ and _____. They created colorful _____ in beautiful patterns using little pieces of _____ clay.
Architecture pages 38–39	Buildings were constructed with bricks made of _____. The Mesopotamians developed the _____ and the _____, and they were some of the first to use _____. They built thick _____ around their cities for _____.

Make a Book Jacket

Choose a topic and follow the steps to plan a book jacket with a partner.

1. The book jacket will be about

   _____.

2. The title of the book is

   _____.

3. The illustration or picture for the front cover will be

   _____.

4. Main ideas for the front flap are

   •

   •

   •

5. The main ideas for the back flap are

   •

   •

   •

6. The main ideas for the back cover are

   •

   •

   •

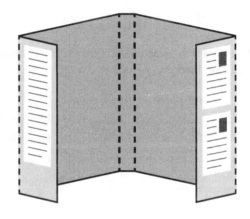

7. Write the name of the person who is working on each part next to the part he is doing.

8. Write a rough draft for the back cover and flaps.

9. Make a final copy of the summary and additional information.

10. Finalize the illustrations.

11. Fold a piece of construction paper according to the diagram on the instructional aid to include a front, back, spine, and two side panels.

12. Mount the text, title, and illustrations on the book jacket.

13. Check to be sure all of the steps are completed.

Study Guide

Match each term about Mesopotamia with its definition.

_____ 1. studying the movements and position of the sun, moon, stars, and planets in the belief that they influence people's lives

_____ 2. developed by using the cycles of the moon

_____ 3. allowed farmers to drop seeds down a funnel on the center of the plow

_____ 4. used to sign documents and record information

_____ 5. the scientific study of the stars and heavenly objects

_____ 6. came from the development of a number system based on a certain number

_____ 7. wedge-shaped writing

_____ 8. the Mesopotamians were the first people to recognize the concept of this numeral

_____ 9. smallest unit of weight

_____ 10. improved transportation by land

A	seeder plow
B	astrology
C	barley-corn
D	wheel
E	astronomy
F	zero
G	cylinder seal
H	60-minute hour
I	cuneiform
J	twelve-month calendar

Write _True_ if the statement is true. If the statement is false, write the correction for the underlined words.

_____ 11. Music was <u>unimportant</u> to religious rituals and daily work.

_____ 12. <u>Epics</u> were written about Sumerian gods and about military victories.

_____ 13. Utnapishtim tells how he built a ship and gathered aboard his family in the _Epic of <u>Gilgamesh</u>_.

_____ 14. Ancient civilizations developed their own <u>mythology</u> by mixing the memory of the Flood with myths.

_____ 15. The historically accurate account of the Flood was revealed to <u>Moses</u> by God.

_____ 16. Mesopotamians made beautiful things with the <u>stone</u> they had.

_____ 17. Buildings were constructed of <u>wood</u>.

_____ 18. Mesopotamians developed the arch and <u>column</u>.

_____ 19. If an enemy attacked, everyone moved inside the <u>turrets</u>.

_____ 20. Houses varied according to the <u>social status</u> of the owner.

Later Mesopotamian Civilizations

_____

Complete the details about each empire.

Civilization	Details
Akkadian Empire pages 40–41	**Capital:** _____ **Main leader(s):** _____ It was the first known _____. The Akkadians borrowed _____ writing, _____ techniques, and _____ from the Sumerians.
Amorite civilization (Babylonian Empire) pages 41–43	**Capital:** _____ **Main leader(s):** _____ Babylon was a _____ of _____. _____ united the land of _____ and was a successful _____ leader. Hammurabi gathered, organized, and simplified _____ laws in a collection known as _____.
Hittite Empire page 44	**Capital:** Hattushash **Main leader(s):** _____ The Hittites _____ in the production of _____. They made the strongest _____ of the time and used horse-drawn _____.
Assyrian Empire pages 44–45	**Capital:** _____ **Main leader(s):** Sargon II and Sennacherib Assyrians spread _____ elements of the _____ and _____ civilizations throughout the _____ world. One of the first _____ was in Nineveh. The Assyrian _____ was equipped with _____ weapons. God described Assyria as a _____ and _____ in His _____ that He would use to punish _____. God showed _____ to the ruthless _____ by sending _____ to _____ to preach _____. The people repented, but they eventually returned to their _____ ways, and God _____ them.
Chaldean Empire (New Babylonian Empire) pages 46–47	**Capital:** Babylon **Main leader(s):** _____ The _____ and the _____ destroyed Nineveh. The Chaldean _____ reached its _____ under the reign of _____. He ended up living in the _____ like an _____ because he viewed his own accomplishments with a heart of _____ and failed to respond to God's _____. _____ succeeded Nebuchadnezzar to the throne, and _____ succeeded Nebonidus. God gave Belshazzar a _____ by writing on a _____. God executed _____ against Belshazzar when _____ captured Babylon for the _____.

Study Guide

Mark all the correct answers.

1. The Sumerian civilization declined and fell because
   - ○ Sumer maintained its power and its military knowledge and might.
   - ○ after the death of Ur-Nammu, Sumer weakened from a series of wars with its neighbors.
   - ○ invaders battled for control of Mesopotamia.

2. The Akkadian Empire was established
   - ○ as the first empire.
   - ○ by Sargon I.
   - ○ with Akkad as its capital.

3. Sargon
   - ○ came to power in the city-state of Kish.
   - ○ conquered city-states throughout Mesopotamia.
   - ○ had less authority than the priests.

4. What is true about numbering the years?
   - ○ Years prior to Christ's birth are labeled BC after the year.
   - ○ Years following Christ's birth are labeled AD before the year.
   - ○ *Circa* is written ca. before an approximate date.

5. Scholars who sought to reduce Christ's importance in history decided to label dates after the year as
   - ○ BCE for "before the common era."
   - ○ BC and AD.
   - ○ CE for "common era."

6. The Amorites established
   - ○ the Babylonian Empire.
   - ○ Babylon as the capital of the empire.
   - ○ a center of trade on the Euphrates River.

7. Hammurabi
   - ○ became king of the Amorite kingdom.
   - ○ separated the land of Mesopotamia.
   - ○ wrote a collection of laws called Hammurabi's Code.

Write *True* if the statement is true. If the statement is false, write the correction for the underlined words.

_____ 8. The Mosaic law forbids giving special treatment to <u>poor</u> people.

_____ 9. Under Hammurabi's code, <u>wealthy</u> people were not punished the same as a commoner.

_____ 10. The Mosaic law is <u>God-centered</u>.

_____ 11. The Mosaic law has <u>small</u> sections about how to worship God.

_____ 12. There are <u>many</u> religious sections in Hammurabi's code.

Study Guide

_____

Answer the question.

13. Why is there such a difference between the Mosaic law and Hammurabi's Code? _____

_____

_____

Write *True* if the statement is true. If the statement is false, write the correction for the underlined words.

_____ 14. The Hittites were the descendants of <u>Heth</u>.

_____ 15. A <u>priest</u> ruled the Hittite Empire.

_____ 16. The Hittites excelled in the production of <u>pottery</u>.

_____ 17. The Amorites took control of the <u>Amorite</u> city of Babylon.

_____ 18. Other nations invaded Hittite territory and the rule of the Hittites <u>flourished</u>.

_____ 19. <u>Nineveh</u> became the capital city of the Assyrian Empire.

_____ 20. God used the Assyrians to <u>help</u> His disobedient people.

_____ 21. <u>Jonah</u> preached to the people of Nineveh and the people turned from their evil way.

_____ 22. God <u>blessed</u> the people of Nineveh when they returned to their evil ways.

Label the map.

23. Use a colored pencil to color the map key and the Assyrian Empire.
    Label cities and bodies of water, including the rivers.

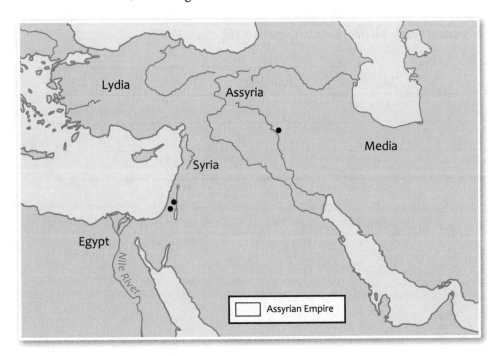

Study Guide

Answer the questions.

24. What was the capital of the Chaldean Empire? _____

_____

_____

25. Who was responsible for the Chaldean Empire reaching its height under the reign of Nebuchadnezzar according to Jeremiah 27:5–7? _____

_____

_____

26. What did God do when Nebuchadnezzar failed to give glory to God for his accomplishments?

_____

_____

_____

27. What was the theme of Nebuchadnezzar's letter after God restored Nebuchadnezzar? _____

_____

_____

_____

_____

_____

28. How does Nebuchadnezzar's letter relate to Genesis 3:15? _____

_____

_____

_____

_____

Navigating the Nile

_____

Fill in the blanks to complete the word for each clue.

1. ___ ___ ___ ___ ___ ___ ___ ___ ___
2. ___ ___ ___ ___ ___ ___ ___
3. ___ ___ ___ ___ ___ ___ ___ ___
4. ___ ___ ___ ___ ___ ___ ___ ___
5. ___ ___ ___ ___ ___
6. ___ ___ ___ ___ ___ ___ ___
7. ___ ___ ___ ___ ___ ___
8. ___ ___ ___ ___ ___ ___
9. ___ ___ ___ ___ ___ ___
10. ___ ___ ___ ___ ___ ___ ___ ___ ___
11. ___ ___ ___ ___ ___ ___ ___ ___ ___ ___ ___
12. ___ ___ ___ ___ ___ ___ ___ ___ ___ ___ ___
13. ___ ___ ___ ___ ___ ___ ___
14. ___ ___ ___ ___ ___ ___ ___ ___ ___

1. Egypt's geography _____ against invasion.

2. The Bible's name for Egypt is _____.

3. Dangerous rapids in the Nile River are called _____.

4. The dangerous sections of the river slowed the advancement of _____.

5. The river's current allowed _____ to sail northward.

6. Egyptians _____ on the Nile for food and water.

7. The river _____ from north to south.

8. Where there was no water in Egypt, there was _____.

9. Wherever the Nile flowed, _____ grew nearby.

10. Sections of the Nile become shallow and rocky, causing _____ rapids.

11. Trade _____ developed where river traffic slowed.

12. Egyptians worshiped the Nile rather than _____ the true God.

13. The Nile is four _____ miles long.

14. Descendants of Mizraim, the _____ of Noah, settled in northeastern Africa.

Since at least 4000 BC, the Nile has been used for irrigation, which is controlled today by the Aswan High Dam.

Use the shaded letters to complete the statement.

15. The Nile River provided _____ for travelers and traders.

Study Guide

Complete the section.

1. Egypt's natural barriers were _____

   _____

2. How did the Nile affect the development of civilization in Egypt? _____

   _____

   _____

   _____

3. How did the flooding of the Nile affect the taxes people paid? _____

   _____

   _____

   _____

4. Compare and contrast how taxes were determined in Egypt with the modern tax system. _____

   _____

   _____

   _____

5. How did the flooding of the Nile affect the development of the calendar? _____

   _____

   _____

   _____

Plan the essay on a sheet of paper, then write it below.

6. Describe how God used Joseph to preserve His people and surrounding civilizations.

   _____

   _____

   _____

   _____

   _____

   _____

   _____

Study Guide

Color the map.

7. Blue: Nile River

8. Green: Mediterranean Sea and Red Sea

9. Yellow: Egypt

10. Red: Sahara

11. Orange: Nile Delta

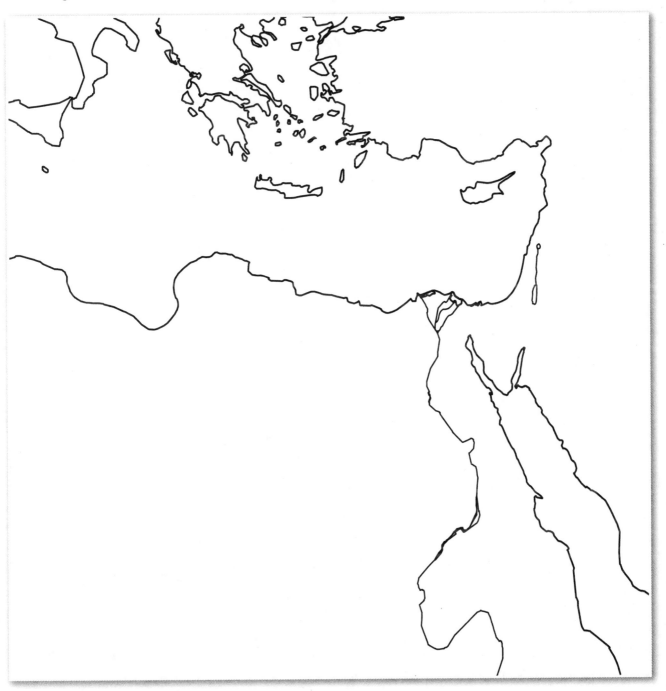

Pyramid Organizer: Old Kingdom

Complete the sentences on the pyramid. Student Text pages are given above each section for reference.

(Student Text p. 55)

1. The area of mountains along the Nile to the south was known as _____ Egypt.

2. The plains around the Nile Delta were known as _____ Egypt.

3. A line of rulers belonging to the same family is a _____.

4. Rulers of Egypt were called _____ and were believed to be _____.

5. The _____ at Giza were built as _____ for pharaohs.

(Student Text p. 56)

6. Baskets, boats, rope, and paper were made from _____.

7. Records and artifacts survived because of Egypt's hot, dry _____.

(Student Text p. 57)

8. Ancient Egyptian writing is called _____.

9. The Egyptian language was unlocked by using the _____.

(Student Text p. 58)

10. Egyptians used their knowledge of anatomy to turn a dead body into a _____.

(Student Text p. 59)

11. French soldiers renamed the *shenu* the _____.

Plan each essay on a sheet of paper. Write the final drafts on a new sheet of paper.

12. Describe the Egyptian pyramid (Student Text page 55). Include a description of two of the rooms inside the pyramid.

13. Describe the mummification process (Student Text page 58).

Hieroglyphics

Hieroglyphics probably began with one picture representing each word, but that system soon became impractical. It changed to have each symbol representing a sound. This is slightly different from the English alphabet in which sounds can be represented by combinations of letters. For instance, "sh" as in *shop* is made in English by combining an *s* and an *h*.

However, there is a symbol in hieroglyphics for the "sh" sound. Also, some English letters can sound like other letters. The *c* in *cat* sounds like a *k*, and the c in *cent* sounds like an *s*. When reading or writing hieroglyphics, remember to think of the English sounds and not just the letters.

Use the key on Student Text page 59 to match the words.

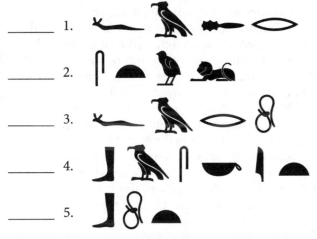

_____ 1.

_____ 2.

_____ 3.

_____ 4.

_____ 5.

A	basket
B	boat
C	father
D	pharaoh
E	stool

Write the correct term in hieroglyphics.

6. Egyptian paper

7. Egyptian tool for dipping water

8. French word used for *shenu*

9. Preserved dead body

10. Longest river in the world

Write your name in hieroglyphics in the cartouche outline.

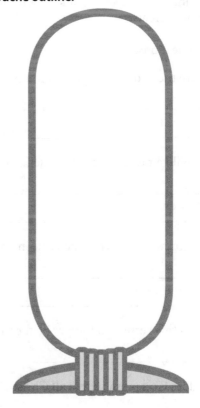

Kinds of Mummies

Read the information.

The Egyptians were not the only civilization that mummified their dead. The oldest mummies actually came from the other side of the globe in Chile and Peru. The bodies in South America were preserved by either drying them in the hot sun or freezing them in the cold temperatures of the Andes Mountains. The Egyptians laid the bodies out flat. The South American mummies are in crouched positions with their knees pulled up to their chins. Both the South Americans and the Egyptians wrapped the mummies in layers of cloth. The South Americans used cotton and wool cloth, while the Egyptians used linen. In South America, sometimes the wrapped bodies were topped with false heads made of painted cloth stuffed with leaves and covered with a wig of human hair.

Many other mummies have been discovered that were not mummified on purpose. Weather conditions and location contributed to the process. Across northern Europe, many ancient bodies have been discovered in swampy bogs, well preserved by the cold conditions. These mummies are named according to where they are found. One such mummy is called the Lindow Man. Scientists have been able to learn many things about what his lifestyle was like. They have determined that he did very little manual labor, that his beard was trimmed with shears, and that his last meal was unleavened bread.

Ice mummies are another type of mummy. A dead body was discovered high in the Italian Alps. He had an unfinished bow, some arrows, a wooden ax with a metal head, and all the materials needed to make a fire. He appeared to have been buried for over four thousand years. Historians are uncertain why the man was so high in the Alps in what would have been very bad conditions. He had head wounds and arrow wounds. Scientists think that someone may have been pursuing him when he got caught in a snowstorm.

In Greenland, eight Inuit mummies were found in a cave, dressed in warm clothes and lying on sealskin blankets. Around them were goods needed to journey into the afterlife. Freezing temperatures preserved these mummies for over five hundred years.

Through cryonics, a modern mummy is made, but it is quite different from an ancient mummy. The purpose is not to preserve the body for the afterlife. The hope is that the sick person can be preserved and restored when a cure has been found. After a person dies, scientists called cryonicists freeze the brain. The body is cooled and the blood is replaced with a blood substitute. The body's temperature is lowered to −223.6°F, and the body is stored in a container of liquid nitrogen. People pay significant amounts of money to have their bodies frozen; however, there is no proof that cryonics actually works.

Answer the questions.

1. What are the two basic types of mummies? _____

_____

_____

2. Why would a person subject himself to cryonics? _____

_____

_____

3. Read Hebrews 9:27. Write the verse in your own words. _____

_____

_____

4. Based on this verse, what might be the main goal of the people being frozen? _____

_____

5. What does God promise that all Christians will receive after the resurrection (Philippians 3:20–21)?

_____

Pyramid Organizer: Middle Kingdom _____

Refer to page 60 to complete the sentences on the pyramid.

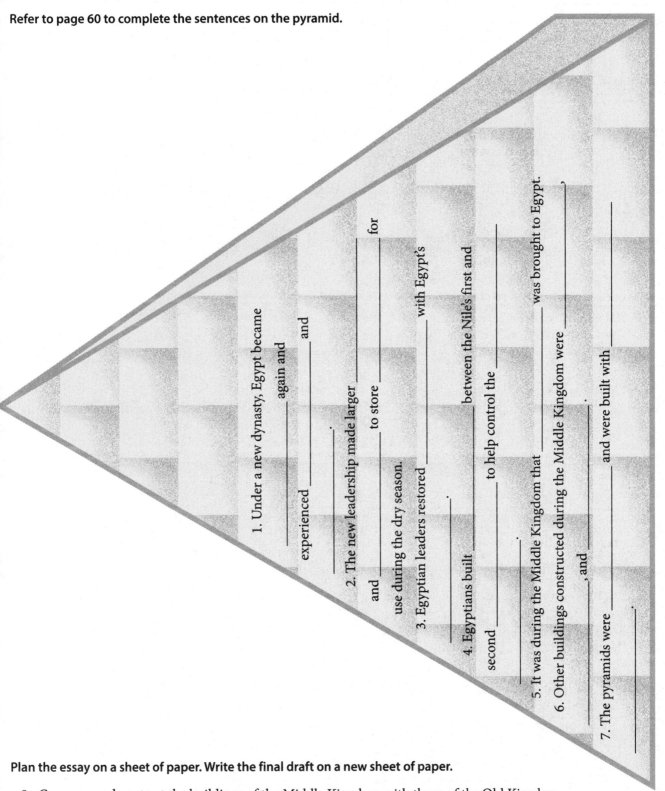

1. Under a new dynasty, Egypt became _____ again and _____ and experienced _____.

2. The new leadership made larger _____ and _____ to store _____ for use during the dry season.

3. Egyptian leaders restored _____ with Egypt's _____.

4. Egyptians built _____ between the Nile's first and second _____ to help control the _____.

5. It was during the Middle Kingdom that _____ was brought to Egypt.

6. Other buildings constructed during the Middle Kingdom were _____, and _____.

7. The pyramids were _____ and were built with _____.

Plan the essay on a sheet of paper. Write the final draft on a new sheet of paper.

8. Compare and contrast the buildings of the Middle Kingdom with those of the Old Kingdom.

Pyramid Organizer: New Kingdom

Refer to pages 61–62 to complete the sentences on the pyramid.

1. The Egyptians were conquered by the _____, who introduced _____ and _____ weapons and _____ horse-drawn _____.

2. God instructed _____ to tell Pharaoh to let the _____ go.

3. During this period, the pharaohs were _____ kings.

4. Pharaohs expanded Egypt's _____ by _____ neighboring peoples.

5. They gained wealth by _____ and _____ with other civilizations to obtain _____.

6. The regent, _____, crowned herself pharaoh, giving her more control over Egypt.

7. Egypt's greatest warrior king was _____ .

8. The pharaoh _____ began his rule at age _____ and is most famous for _____ his tomb.

9. Historians have extensive information about how pharaohs lived and died through _____ discoveries.

10. One of the last pharaohs of this period was _____, who defeated the _____ .

Plan the essay on a sheet of paper. Write the final draft on a new sheet of paper.

11. Compare the importance of Howard Carter's contribution to the study of Egypt and the importance of Leonard Woolley's contribution to the study of Sumer.

Study Guide

_____

Write *O* for Old Kingdom, *M* for Middle Kingdom, and *N* for New Kingdom.

_____ 1. All of Pharaoh's army was destroyed in the Red Sea.

_____ 2. Egyptians experienced peace and stability.

_____ 3. This was known as "the Age of Pyramids."

Answer the questions.

4. What are the names for the two areas along the Nile that were settled by the Egyptians? What were the names based on? _____

_____

5. For what purpose were the pyramids at Giza built? _____

_____

6. In what ways was papyrus useful to the Egyptians, and why has much of it survived to today?

_____

_____

7. Why is the Rosetta stone important? _____

_____

_____

_____

Number the steps in the Egyptian mummification process.

_____ 8. Once removed from the natron, the body was washed and wrapped in linen strips.

_____ 9. The embalmer placed the organs in canopic jars.

_____ 10. The embalmer cleaned out the skull.

_____ 11. The body was soaked in natron for seventy days.

_____ 12. The embalmer cleaned out the abdominal cavities and dried the liver, stomach, lungs, and intestines.

_____ 13. The body was filled with spices.

Match the description to the correct person.

_____ 14. one of the last pharaohs of Egypt; known as the Great

_____ 15. Egyptologist who translated hieroglyphics on the Rosetta stone

_____ 16. pharaoh of Egypt at age nine; known for his tomb treasures

_____ 17. archaeologist who discovered and cataloged King Tut's tomb

A Tutankhamun
B Howard Carter
C Rameses II
D Jean-François Champollion

Plan the essay on a sheet of paper. Then write it on a new sheet of paper.

18. Explain the significance of Moses to Egyptian history.

Ancient Egypt

Complete the section.

Topic	Details
Social classes page 63	An Egyptian's social class depended on his _____ or _____. Farmers, merchants, servants, and slaves were at the _____ of Egypt's social pyramid. The next level included _____, soldiers, _____, and artisans. The next level included the _____ and the pharaoh's _____ and viziers. At the top was the _____ and his family.
Music page 63	Religious ceremonies used songs in _____ and prayer to the gods. One of the main themes in Egyptian music was the _____.
Daily life page 64	Egyptian food consisted of bread from _____ or barley, melons, _____, onions, _____, and figs. The river provided _____ and _____. Egyptians also raised _____ for meat. Clothing was made from _____, cotton, _____, and cloth woven from _____, a type of plant. Egyptians were known for their _____. Ancient _____ were found in some Egyptian ruins. Both men and women wore _____ made from human hair. _____ were also popular, one of which was a black powder called _____. Boys of _____ families went to school.
Religion page 65	Egyptians practiced _____. Families built _____ in their houses to _____ their favorite gods. The Egyptians believed that, after death, they traveled to the _____ of _____, where the god _____ presided. Anubis, the _____-_____ god, weighed the dead person's _____ against the _____ of _____.
Religion page 68	Egyptians believed that the pharaoh was the son of _____. They believed the pharaoh was a _____ and the high _____ of Egypt. Egyptians believed they would be _____ on whether they lived according to the _____ and _____ that the gods had put into the world. If their works were _____ enough, they would spend the _____ in a place of _____. But the Bible teaches that no one will be declared _____ before God on the basis of _____. No _____ works meet God's _____ standard of justice.

Egyptian Religion in Daily Life

Complete the chart.

Egyptian religious practices	Examples of Practices	Inferences about the significance of religion in the daily lives of the Egyptians
Religious symbols		
Religious art		
Rituals		

Study Guide

Write occupations people did for each level of the Egyptian social pyramid.

1.

2.

3.

4.

Write *True* if the statement is true. If the statement is false, write the correction for the underlined words.

_____ 5. An Egyptian's social class depended on his wealth or <u>education</u>.

_____ 6. Anyone from a lower class could rise to a higher class if he gained the <u>pharaoh's</u> favor.

_____ 7. Egyptians <u>disliked</u> music.

_____ 8. One of the main themes in Egyptian music was the <u>Nile</u>.

_____ 9. Egyptians were known for <u>cleanliness</u>.

_____ 10. Egyptian men wore <u>robes</u> that wrapped around their waists.

_____ 11. Women wore long, sleeveless <u>dresses</u>.

_____ 12. Both men and women wore wigs, <u>cosmetics</u>, and necklaces.

_____ 13. Men were <u>long-haired</u> or wore their hair cropped above their shoulders.

_____ 14. Egyptians believed an <u>amulet</u> protected its wearer against evil spirits.

_____ 15. Boys of <u>middle-class</u> families started school at age four or five.

Write the correct name or term next to each clue.

_____ 16. Amenhotep IV changed his name to this

_____ 17. a jackal-headed god that Egyptians believed weighed a dead person's heart

_____ 18. Egyptian god of the underworld

_____ 19. awakened, washed, fed, and put makeup on the idol of Horus

_____ 20. name given to two gods after they were joined during the Middle Kingdom

_____ 21. three gods that formed a model family that Egyptians tried to imitate

_____

_____

Study Guide

_____

Mark all the correct answers.

22. Egyptians believed that a dead person
    - ○ traveled by boat to the Hall of Judgment.
    - ○ should have a copy of the Book of the Dead buried with him.
    - ○ would chant from a portion of text to declare his innocence during judgment.

23. The Egyptian civilization
    - ○ was marred by false religion and injustice.
    - ○ gave glory to God for its achievements.
    - ○ was judged by God for its pride.

Plan the essay on a sheet of paper. Write the final draft below.

24. Compare and contrast Egyptian polytheism with biblical truth. Include at least three differences.

_____

_____

_____

_____

_____

_____

_____

_____

_____

_____

_____

_____

_____

_____

_____

_____

_____

_____

_____

_____

_____

_____

_____

Comparing and Contrasting

Read and follow the steps.

1. Work with a partner to compare and contrast Egypt with Mesopotamia. Use the Student Text and other resources.
2. Complete the diagram with the information that compares and contrasts these two civilizations.
3. Share your information.

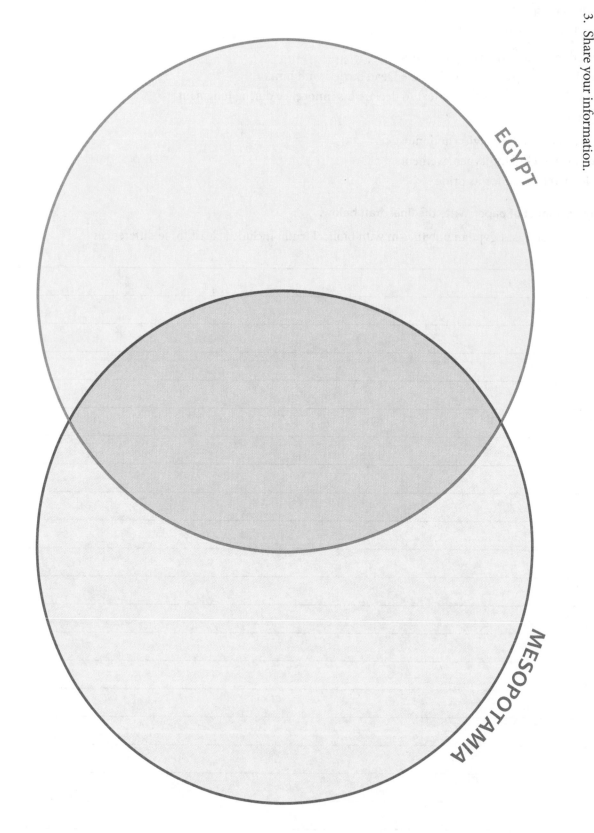

EGYPT

MESOPOTAMIA

Pyramid Organizer: Kush

Refer to pages 69–73 to complete the sentences on the pyramid. Then cut out all four pyramid organizers and put them together by gluing or taping the tabs.

1. Like Egypt, Kush depended on the _____ for food, water, _____, and _____.

2. Like Egypt, they used a _____ and an _____ to farm more land.

3. Kush had an abundance of _____, including _____, copper, _____, ebony, and _____ and more _____.

4. As the Kushites became _____ numerous, the Egyptians feared their growing _____.

5. Kush developed two systems of written language, a form of _____ and a script called _____.

6. Kush developed into a civilization with settlements at _____, and _____, and over time the people of Kush adopted the _____.

7. Kush was conquered by _____, and established a capital at _____.

8. Kush established its independence from _____ and were conquered by the _____.

9. The Kushites exhausted their _____.

Study Guide

_____

Complete the section.

1. Describe the two forms of writing that the Kushites used. _____

_____

_____

_____

2. What happened when the Egyptians conquered the Kushites? _____

_____

_____

_____

3. What contributed to Kush's wealth? _____

_____

_____

_____

4. What happened regarding resources at the time of Kush's decline? _____

_____

5. How did the loss of resources affect the economy? _____

6. How did archaeologists save the temples at Abu Simbel? _____

7. Name two advantages and two disadvantages of the Aswan High Dam.

Advantages	Disadvantages

Study Guide

Write the names of the numbered places on the map.

8. _____

9. _____

10. _____

11. _____

12. _____

13. _____

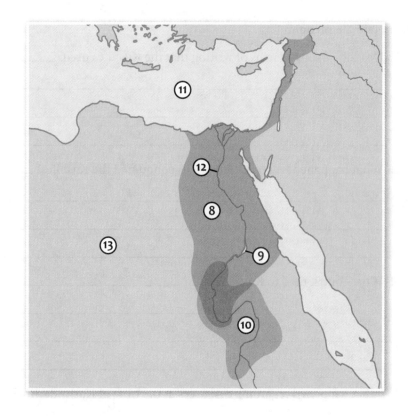

Plan the essay on your own paper. Write the final draft below.

14. Compare the Kushite civilization with the Egyptian civilization.

_____

_____

_____

_____

_____

_____

_____

_____

_____

Ancient Israel

_____

Refer to the Student Text pages 76–78 to complete the chart.

Main Idea	Details
God made many promises to Abraham in the _____ _____.	God promised Abraham that his _____ would become a great _____. God promised to bless _____ and _____ the nations of the _____ would be blessed through him. _____, a descendant of Abraham, would offer the blessing of _____ to all people.
Abraham was the father of the nation of _____.	At first, God chose only _____ among Abraham's sons, and among Isaac's sons, only _____ was chosen. But then God chose all of Jacob's _____ sons to inherit the _____. The twelve tribes that came from them formed a new _____. This nation was called _____ because that was a special name that God had given _____.
_____ was the land where Israel grew from a family into a nation.	After about four hundred years in Egypt, the families of _____ and his sons had grown into a _____ _____.
The _____ was the time when the _____ left Egypt.	Moses told the _____ to let God's people go. Because Pharaoh did not let them go, God unleashed _____ _____ on Egypt. God wanted the _____, the _____, and all _____ to know that He is the one _____ God. The ten plagues ended with a final _____ on Egypt in which all the _____ in the land were killed. God told the Israelites to _____ the blood of a sacrificed _____ on each _____ and on the _____ above the door. Their _____ protected them from _____ when God judged Egypt. The Jews still remember this event during a holiday called _____. After the death of the pharaoh's _____, the ruler _____ to let the Israelites leave Egypt.
Moses led the nation of Israel into the _____ _____.	The nation _____ at the base of Mount Sinai, and _____ declared that Israel was to be a nation set _____ from all other nations. Israel was to _____ these nations to the _____ God. In this way, Israel would be a _____ to them.

Ancient Israel

Refer to the Student Text pages 79–80 to complete the chart.

Main Idea	Details
God gave the nation of Israel His law through _____. It was known as the Mosaic _____.	God commanded the Israelites to _____ His law. The Mosaic law had laws about what activities led a person to be considered _____ or _____. These laws were like _____ lessons. The need for continual _____ from uncleanliness reminded the people of the continual need for cleansing from _____. If the people of Israel obeyed the Mosaic law, God promised to _____ them. But if the Israelites chose to disobey, God promised to _____ the nation of Israel with _____, _____ _____, and _____. Israel's history under the Mosaic Covenant shows that it is _____ to keep all of God's law with one's _____ _____. God gave the Israelites the Mosaic Covenant so other nations could see the _____ and _____ of God.
God wanted a _____ to be built as a symbol of God's presence with His people.	The priests offered a daily _____ for the sins of the Israelites. Once each year, the high priest entered the most holy place in the tabernacle and sprinkled the _____ of a sacrificed animal on the _____ of the _____. The tabernacle was built according to _____ _____. The items in the tabernacle were a symbol of God's _____, _____, and other attributes.
The main characteristic of the Israelite religion was _____.	The Hebrew name for the one true God is _____. The tabernacle was the center of _____ for God's people. Three times a year, all the men of Israel traveled to Jerusalem for the Feast of _____ _____ (Passover), the Feast of _____, and the Feast of _____. The Day of Atonement was the one day every year that the _____ _____ could enter the most sacred room in the tabernacle or temple, the _____ of _____. The act of _____ blood on the ark of the covenant symbolized the _____ for the people's _____. True atonement was made by Christ's sacrificial _____ on the cross.

Online Research

Read the information.

Online research is a way to learn more about a subject. The first step in doing online research is to choose a topic. A teacher or librarian can help select keywords that will give the desired search results about the topic. Enter the keywords in a search engine. Then adjust or narrow the search as needed. A teacher can suggest websites for the student that are suitable by age or grade level.

Always evaluate online sources. Be sure to check the URL ending. Is it .com, .edu, .gov, or .org? For a fact-based report, using a website from a college, museum, or government agency would be more academic. Not all facts on the web are accurate. It is important to check at least three different sources to see if the facts agree.

Remember to consider the author's worldview. Although information on a website may seem right, it is vital to check for bias. Personal websites or blogs should be avoided, as they often contain authors' personal opinions or points of view.

A key step in doing online research is to take careful notes and cite the sources that are used. A site will often list sources for the information it gives. Students should turn in bibliographies of sources and URL logs for sites they use while doing research.

The final step for doing online research involves organizing the research notes to develop concepts and draw conclusions. Avoid *plagiarism* by using words and terms that are different from the research sources. Present the material accurately through a report or project.

Complete the flow chart.

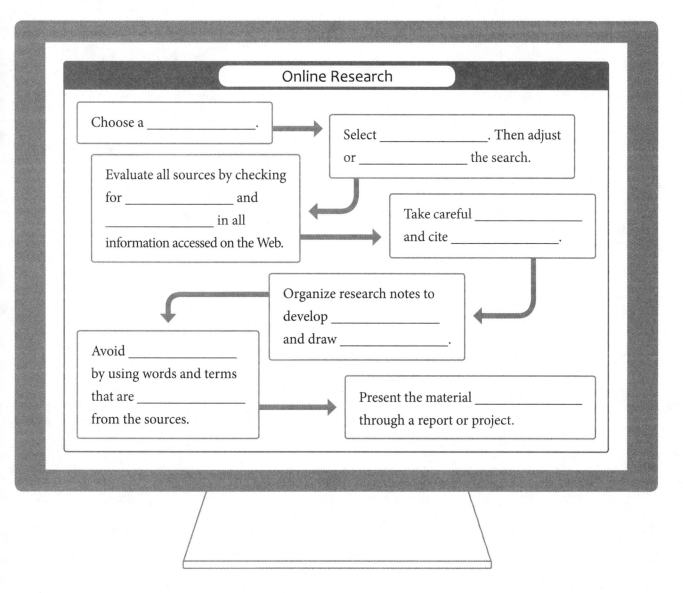

Online Research

Choose a _____.

Select _____. Then adjust or _____ the search.

Evaluate all sources by checking for _____ and _____ in all information accessed on the Web.

Take careful _____ and cite _____.

Organize research notes to develop _____ and draw _____.

Avoid _____ by using words and terms that are _____ from the sources.

Present the material _____ through a report or project.

Tabernacle Furnishings

Choose a tabernacle furnishing from the chart below.
Write its name in the chart title.

Furnishing	Altar of burnt offering	Altar of incense	Ark of the covenant	Golden lampstand	Laver	Table of showbread
Bible Verses	Exodus 27:1–8 38:1–7 40:29	Exodus 30:1–10 37:25–28	Exodus 25:10–22 26:33–34 37:1–9	Exodus 25:31–40 26:35 37:17–24	Exodus 30:18 38:8 40:7	Exodus 25:23–30 26:35 37:10–16

Refer to the Bible verses and other sources to write notes about the tabernacle furnishing.
Refer to the notes to make the model.

Tabernacle Furnishing:			
Appearance	Dimensions (cubit = 20.4 in.)	Purpose	Location (court, holy place, or holy of holies)

Format the report as a museum identification card. Include the details about the tabernacle furnishing. Write a rough draft of the report below. Then, write the final version on a note card. Display the card with the model.

_____

_____

_____

_____

_____

_____

_____

_____

_____

_____

_____

Ancient Israel

Refer to the Student Text pages 82 and 85 to complete the chart.

Main Idea	Details
Before the Israelites could live in the land of Canaan, they had to _____ it.	Moses' successor, _____, led the Israelites to _____ God and conquer _____. God helped the Israelites by parting the _____ River. He also caused the walls of _____ to fall. Under Joshua's _____, the people of _____ were able to conquer the land.
The Israelites did not show the nations the _____ of God by living _____ to His laws.	For more than three hundred years, there was a pattern of disobedience and _____ followed by God raising up a _____ to lead Israel in _____ and deliverance.
The Israelites became more and more like the wicked _____ around them.	They began to worship the same _____ _____ and to commit the same _____. God _____ them by sending other nations to _____ over parts of Israel. When the Israelites cried out for _____, God sent _____. Each time, the Israelites went back to doing _____ and suffered _____ from their enemies.
Israel had _____ forms of government in its history.	During the wilderness wanderings, _____ was the leader of the nation of _____. When the people were settled in the land, _____ and _____ were governed by _____. God also raised up _____ to deliver His people from oppressive _____. Beginning with Saul, Israel was governed by _____.
God made a covenant with David called the _____ _____.	God promised that David would have a _____ name. David's dynasty would last _____, and God would be a _____ to the Davidic kings. If David's _____ disobeyed God, they would be _____.

Costs and Benefits

Choose an account to evaluate. Circle the account.

Israelites ask for a king
1 Samuel 8:4–22
Deuteronomy 17:14–20

Fiery furnace
Daniel 3:1–30

Daniel in the lions' den
Daniel 6:1–28

Identify the people and the choice that was made.

People involved

_____

_____

_____

Choice that was made

_____

_____

_____

Complete the chart.

Costs	Benefits

Write a paragraph analyzing the decision that was made. Include an application to decision making in your own life.

_____

_____

_____

_____

Study Guide

Complete the section.

1. Explain why Abraham is considered to be the father of the nation of Israel. _____

_____

_____

_____

2. How does the Davidic Covenant relate to the Abrahamic Covenant? _____

_____

_____

_____

_____

_____

_____

3. What cultural ideas and practices of ancient Israel were evident during the Exodus? _____

_____

_____

_____

4. What was the Mosaic Covenant, and how did it impact the people of ancient Israel as well as other people?

_____

_____

_____

5. How did the Israelites worship God in the wilderness? _____

_____

_____

_____

6. What did the Israelites believe about God? _____

7. What became the center of worship for God's people after the tabernacle? _____

Study Guide

_____

Complete the chart.

8–10. Write the name, purpose, and length of each of Israel's feasts.

Feast	Purpose	Duration

Complete the map according to the directions below.
Shade the map key and the map with the following colors.

11. Light brown—the extent of David's
    and Solomon's kingdoms

12. Light green—Israel today

Write the number that corresponds with each country
in the correct location on the map.

13. Israel

14. Jordan

15. Lebanon

16. Syria

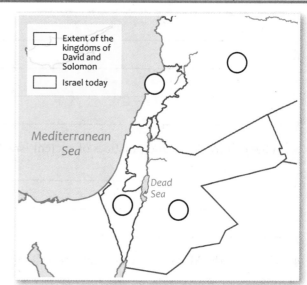

Mark all the correct answers.

17. When God led the Israelites from Sinai to the edge of Canaan,

    ○ they thanked God for His care of them.
    ○ the people lacked faith and complained.
    ○ the Israelites wandered in the wilderness for forty years because they did not trust God.

18. Before the Israelites could live in Canaan, they

    ○ had to conquer it.
    ○ had to purge the people of Canaan from the land.
    ○ were expected to obey God in order for God to do miraculous works on their behalf.

19. When they conquered the land, the people of Israel failed to obey by

    ○ allowing some of the people who lived there to remain alive.
    ○ living according to God's laws.
    ○ becoming like the wicked nations around them.

20. The Israelites' disobedience led to

    ○ punishment followed by God raising a judge to bring the people to repentance.
    ○ their asking Samuel to give them a king.
    ○ other nations ruling over parts of Israel.

Ancient Israel

_____

Refer to the Student Text pages 86–87 to complete the chart.

Main Idea	Details
The kingdom of Israel _____ after Rehoboam said that he would rule them more _____.	The ten northern tribes followed _____ and formed the _____ _____. The two southern tribes, Judah and Benjamin, stayed under _____ rule and established the _____ _____.
The northern tribes kept the name _____, and Jeroboam established his capital at Samaria.	Jeroboam made two _____ _____ and said they were the _____ of Israel. Israel advanced economically because of heavy _____, _____ _____, and _____.
The tribes of the Southern Kingdom took the name _____ and kept the capital at _____.	Judah's kings all descended from _____. A few of Judah's rulers lived _____ before God, but many were _____. God's people had corrupted _____ worship of _____ by mixing with it the _____ worship of the _____ around them.
In 586 BC, King _____ conquered Judah.	He _____ Jerusalem. He took more than ten thousand people away to _____ in Babylon. The dispersion of the Israelites is called the _____.
God would make a _____ Covenant.	God would restore the Israelites to their _____. He promised to give His _____ _____ and to transform the hearts of His people to _____ and _____ Him.
The Assyrians relocated the _____ and _____ people from the northern tribes of Israel.	These Israelites were assimilated into the Assyrian _____.
King Nebuchadnezzar relocated the southern tribes of Judah to _____.	The Jews were allowed to retain their _____ and cultural _____.
Cyrus _____ Babylon.	Cyrus allowed the Jews to _____ to Judea.
_____ wanted to kill all the Jews.	King Xerxes gave the Jews permission to _____ themselves. Xerxes ordered the _____ of Haman.

Comparing Historical Maps

Compare the maps to answer the questions.

1. Which map shows Israel as a united kingdom? _____

2. What kingdoms were formed when Israel was no longer united? _____

3. What four areas did Israel lose when the kingdom became divided? _____

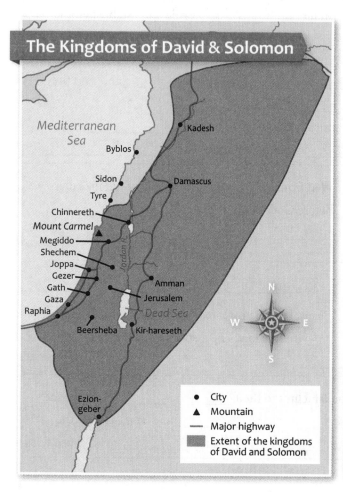

Look at the map "The Kingdoms of Israel & Judah" to answer the questions.

_____ 4. After Israel was divided, which kingdom was located west of the Dead Sea?

_____ 5. In which kingdom is the King's Highway shown?

_____ 6. Which kingdom is next to the Sea of Galilee?

_____ 7. In which kingdom is Jerusalem located?

_____ 8. Which kingdom does the Jordan River run through?

Ancient Israel

Refer to the Student Text pages 88–89 to complete the chart.

Main Idea	Details
The Jews returned from captivity in Babylon in _____.	One group led by Zerubbabel rebuilt the _____. Ezra returned to _____ with another group of Jews. He taught the people the _____. Nehemiah returned with another group of Jews, and he led the _____ of the _____ of Jerusalem.
The Greeks conquered the _____. Judea became part of the Greek _____.	_____ was ruled by the Ptolemies. _____ was ruled by the Seleucids.
Greek had become a _____ language.	A Greek translation of the Old Testament Scriptures was called the _____.
Many Jews living under Greek rule adopted the _____ and _____ of the Greeks.	The _____, who were appointed by the Greek rulers, promoted the _____ lifestyle of the Greeks. Some Jews began to insist on a strict observance of the _____.
The Seleucid king _____ became ruler of Judea.	When he was away fighting in Egypt, the Jews attempted to _____ his appointed _____. Antiochus tore down the city _____ and defiled the temple.
Jews who followed the _____ were not willing to accept the destruction of their _____.	Judas _____ led attacks and _____ the Seleucids. He led his army to _____. They _____ and _____ the temple. The rededication was celebrated for _____ days.
The Jews were able to _____ their kingdom.	This dynasty's kings were _____ and highly influenced by Greek culture. Two groups became _____ in Judea. The Pharisees stressed _____ of life and _____ to the Torah. They opposed the current _____. The Sadducees were more _____ among the priests and rulers of Judea. They worked with the new rulers, the _____. This sometimes involved _____ and _____.

Study Guide

_____

Answer the questions.

1. What caused the kingdom of Israel to split? _____

   _____

   _____

   _____

2. Describe the kingdoms that resulted from the split. _____

   _____

   _____

   _____

3. In what ways did both kingdoms depart from true worship of God? _____

   _____

   _____

   _____

Mark all the correct answers.

4. Prophets were called by God to
   - forsake idolatry.
   - stop injustices that were caused by using wealth and power to oppress others.
   - urge His people back to fellowship with Him.

5. Because the Israelites did not listen to the prophets' warnings,
   - judgment came in 722 BC.
   - the Israelites conquered the Assyrians.
   - the people of Israel were conquered by the Assyrians and carried away as captives.

6. During the Diaspora,
   - Jews dispersed to other countries.
   - Nebuchadnezzar conquered Judah and destroyed Jerusalem, including the temple.
   - more than ten thousand people were carried away to exile in Babylon.

Answer the question.

7. Analyze the New Covenant and its effects on its beneficiaries. _____

   _____

   _____

   _____

   _____

   _____

Study Guide

_____

Write _True_ if the statement is true. If the statement is false, write the correction for the underlined words.

_____ 8. When the Greeks conquered the Persians, <u>Judea</u> became part of the Greek Empire.

_____ 9. When Alexander the Great's kingdom was divided, <u>Judea</u> lay on the border between Egypt and Syria.

_____ 10. As Egypt and Syria fought each other, Judea was <u>never</u> under the rule of one or the other.

_____ 11. <u>Hebrew</u> became a common language.

_____ 12. The Septuagint made the Old Testament available to <u>Gentiles</u> and to Jews who did not speak Hebrew.

_____ 13. The Jews living under Greek rule <u>shunned</u> the customs and lifestyle of the Greeks.

_____ 14. The high priests often <u>denounced</u> the sinful lifestyle of the Greeks.

_____ 15. Antiochus greatly <u>offended</u> the Jews by entering the temple and seizing its treasures and sacred vessels.

_____ 16. While Antiochus was fighting in Egypt, the Jews tried to <u>understand</u> his appointed leaders.

_____ 17. Antiochus put Jews to death for keeping the Sabbath or for owning a copy of the <u>Torah</u>.

_____ 18. <u>Judas Maccabeus</u> led a revolt against the Seleucids.

_____ 19. The rededication of the temple was celebrated by the festival called <u>Hanukkah</u>.

Mark all the correct answers.

20. After the Seleucid Empire was not able to keep the Jews under its rule,

  ○ the Jews were able to reestablish their kingdom.
  ○ a dynasty of kings who were ruthless and highly influenced by Greek culture developed.
  ○ two groups became important in Judea.

21. The Pharisees

  ○ continued to stress purity of life and obedience to the Torah.
  ○ opposed the current rulers.
  ○ were just when they laid heavy burdens on people.

22. The Sadducees

  ○ were less influential among the priests and rulers of Judea than the Pharisees were.
  ○ saw the importance of power in preserving the Jewish people and their worship at the temple.
  ○ worked with the Romans, which sometimes involved corruption and injustice.

Ancient Israel

_____

Refer to the Student Text pages 93–94 to complete the chart.

Main Idea	Details
The Jews believed the Messiah would descend from _____ and would come to _____ all the wrongs they had suffered.	Jesus was born in the _____ line of David. Angels identified Him as the _____ of the Jews. Jesus identified Himself as the _____, or the Christ. As the _____ of David, Jesus is King. One day He will return to _____ on the earth and to put an end to all _____.
Neither Jews nor anyone else could completely _____ the law that God revealed in the Mosaic _____.	This showed the _____ of people and the need for a savior.
Jesus, a descendant of Abraham, would bring _____ to all the _____ of the earth.	He brought blessing by being the _____ for sins. Jesus paid the _____ for sin and offers _____ to those who trust in Him.
The Holy Spirit fulfills the promises of the _____ Covenant.	The Holy Spirit can change _____.
The prophecies about God delivering His people through a Messiah were fulfilled by _____.	Jesus performed _____ and _____ that the kingdom of God was near. He taught that He was _____ and also _____.
The message of Jesus included the need for _____.	Jesus told the people that the _____ of their problems was _____. They would have to repent of their sins to be included in the _____ of _____.
The _____ did not recognize Jesus as the Messiah.	The religious leaders accused Jesus of being against _____. The Romans listened to the Pharisees and Sadducees and _____ Jesus.
Archaeologists uncovered a limestone block with an inscription at _____.	The inscription was part of a dedication to Tiberius Caesar from "Pontius Pilate, _____ [governor] of Judea." The Bible records that _____ was the Roman _____ of Judea at the time of Jesus Christ. The limestone is one of the first _____ discovered with Pontius Pilate's name on it.

Ancient Israel

Refer to the Student Text pages 94–95 to complete the chart.

Main Idea	Details
Three days after the death of Jesus, a great _____ happened.	Jesus _____ from the grave and _____ before His followers alive. His death and _____ made salvation available for all people who repent and _____ Him for _____ life.
Jesus ascended back into _____. His followers continued to spread His message of _____.	The followers of Jesus preached the _____ to the people of Israel and to people all over the _____.
There were changes in the _____ practice of religion.	The exile cured the Jews from the sin of _____. During the exile, the _____ became the center of Jewish worship.
The Jews returned to _____ after the exile and rebuilt the _____.	The Jews could offer _____ again. The synagogue remained a part of Jewish _____.
After _____ destroyed the second _____, Judaism underwent a further change.	The _____ practiced rabbinic Judaism, no longer focusing on _____ to atone for one's sin. The focus was on _____ to the law.
The basic beliefs of Judaism include the belief in only one _____ and the belief that His will is revealed in the _____.	The _____ interpreted the Torah. The rabbis believed that _____ were specially chosen by God for salvation. They also believed they needed to obey the _____.

Refer to the Student Text page 95 to complete the chart.

Judaism and the Law	Christianity and the Law
Paul wrote in the book of Romans that Israel had tried to keep the law but had been _____. The Jews were so focused on keeping the _____ that they did not recognize Jesus as the Messiah.	God pronounces _____ on those who do not perfectly obey the law. The _____ message teaches that salvation comes by grace. Jesus kept the _____ and suffered the _____ all people deserve for not keeping it. Every person who calls on Jesus for _____ is no longer _____ for not keeping the law.

Ancient Israel

_____

Refer to the Student Text pages 96–97 to complete the chart.

Main Idea	Details
During the time of Jesus, the rule of Israel shifted to _____ rule.	Roman _____ eventually ruled the entire region.
The extortion by the governors and the Roman _____ caused the Jews to yearn for _____.	_____ were plotting the overthrow of Rome.
The Roman governor _____ took money from the temple treasury.	Two Jews mocked Florus as a _____ _____. Florus had his troops _____, rob, and _____ Jews. The Jews _____. They ambushed and _____ the Romans.
Vespasian conquered the country, surrounding _____.	The Roman Empire plunged into _____, delaying Vespasian's _____ on Jerusalem.
Jesus predicted the _____ of Jerusalem.	God would pour out His _____ on His people. Many would be _____, and those who remained would be _____ among the nations. Jerusalem would be under the _____.
In AD 70, Titus and the Roman army _____ Jerusalem.	They stayed in their _____ and waited for months. The Jews could not _____ their city, and no one could _____. The Romans waited until the city suffered from _____. After the Romans _____ _____ the walls, they _____ through Jerusalem. After two months, the city was _____ by Romans.
After Jerusalem was destroyed, three _____ remained.	The first two strongholds fell by AD 72. The third stronghold was a mountaintop _____ called _____. The Zealot Jews had taken refuge there. The winding narrow path to the top _____ the attacking army from _____ them.
The _____ did not give up conquering Masada.	The Romans reached the _____ of one of the _____ of Masada. The Jews committed mass _____.
Israel ceased to exist as a nation.	In 1948, Israel was _____ as a nation.

Study Guide

Complete the section.

1. How did Jesus of Nazareth fulfill the messianic promises expressed in the Old Testament covenants?

_____

_____

_____

_____

_____

_____

2. Explain how archaeological evidence lends support to Pontius Pilate's role as prefect in Judea.

_____

_____

_____

_____

_____

_____

3. Contrast Judaism with the revealed religion of the Old Testament.

_____

_____

_____

_____

_____

_____

4. Analyze the impact of Roman rule on the nation of Israel.

_____

_____

_____

_____

_____

_____

Study Guide

Number the events in the correct order.

_____ Zealots plotted to overthrow Rome through military action.

_____ A rebellion erupted against Florus.

_____ The Zealot Jews died when the Romans besieged Masada.

_____ Vespasian and his Roman legions conquered the country surrounding Jerusalem.

_____ Israel ceased to exist as a nation.

_____ The nation of Israel was reborn.

_____ Israel shifted from the Herodian dynasty to Roman rule.

_____ Titus and his army surrounded Jerusalem.

_____ Florus robbed the temple and used brutality against the Jews.

_____ The Jews ambushed and defeated the Romans during their rebellion against Florus.

_____ Jerusalem and the temple were destroyed.

Define each term.

16. Josephus _____

_____

17. synagogue _____

_____

18. rabbi _____

_____

19. legion _____

_____

20. Judaism _____

_____

Ancient India

Write words to complete the web.

Organized Cities and Government
page 100

The sister cities of _____
and _____ were part of
the _____ civilization.

Environment
page 100

For about eight hundred years, ancient Indians
flourished in the fertile _____
_____. Because of its closeness to
the _____, the land was good for
_____ and for raising _____.

The Harappan Civilization

Religion
page 101

The _____
_____ was a large public
_____ that many historians
believe was used for _____
_____.

Job Specialization
page 101

Along the streets in _____,
the _____ seemed to
be middle-class _____,
probably owned by _____
and _____.

Arts, Sciences, and Written Language
pages 100–101

The Harappans had _____-_____ houses with indoor _____,
_____ _____, and an advanced _____ system.
The Indus people used _____ to make _____ and pots.
Many _____ from the Indus people contain _____. These
_____ _____ remain an unsolved _____.

Answer the questions.

1. Who led a team of archaeologists in discovering Harappa and Mohenjo-Daro, and why is this discovery
   significant? _____
   _____

2. What are some possible causes of the disappearance of the Harappans? _____
   _____

India's Landforms

_____

Follow the instructions to complete the section.

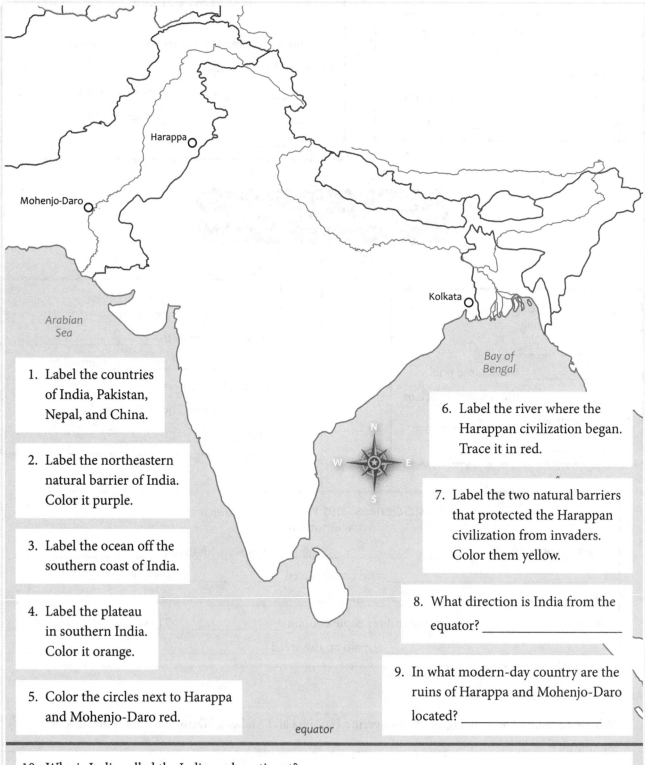

Harappa

Mohenjo-Daro

Kolkata

Arabian
Sea

Bay of
Bengal

1. Label the countries of India, Pakistan, Nepal, and China.

2. Label the northeastern natural barrier of India. Color it purple.

3. Label the ocean off the southern coast of India.

4. Label the plateau in southern India. Color it orange.

5. Color the circles next to Harappa and Mohenjo-Daro red.

6. Label the river where the Harappan civilization began. Trace it in red.

7. Label the two natural barriers that protected the Harappan civilization from invaders. Color them yellow.

8. What direction is India from the equator? _____

9. In what modern-day country are the ruins of Harappa and Mohenjo-Daro located? _____

equator

10. Why is India called the Indian subcontinent?

Site Map

Label sections of your artifact pan to match the site map.
Draw each artifact at the location in which it was found.
Number each artifact on the map.

A	B
C	**D**

Catalog for Artifacts

Number	Description	Material	Dimensions	Weight	Remarks

Ancient India

Complete the web.

Organized Cities and Government
page 104

The Aryans spread across northern _____
and settled in the _____
_____.
The Aryans did not form a strong _____
_____.
Each village was governed by a _____ of
_____ men and a raja.

Social Structure
page 104

Some of the earliest Aryan hymns
refer to _____ as
well as to _____.
The most important man
in an Aryan village was the
_____.

The Aryan Civilization

Arts, Sciences, and Written Language
page 105

The Aryans appreciated _____.
They played the lute, _____, flute,
_____, and _____.
They practiced science and _____.
The Aryans were knowledgeable about
_____.
Aryans are famous for their _____,
poetry, and _____.
The written _____ of the Aryans is
called _____.

Job Specialization
pages 104–5

Some villagers _____
for a living. Cattle breeding was especially
important to the farmer. Cattle was used
to pay _____ and
_____ for their service.
Each village had craftsmen.
_____ made
bronze _____ and
_____.
Agriculture and the
_____ of goods made
_____ likely.

Study Guide

Complete the section.

1. What discovery did Sir John Marshall and a team of archaeologists make in the Indus Valley? _____

   _____

2. What was the significance of the discovery John Marshall and his team made? _____

   _____

3. List the main achievements of the Harappan civilization. _____

   _____

   _____

4. Relate the geography of India to the development of the Harappan civilization. _____

   _____

   _____

5. What are possible reasons for the disappearance of the Harappans? _____

   _____

   _____

6. How is it possible that the ancient Harappans were capable of the accomplishments they made? _____

   _____

   _____

Write _True_ if the statement is true. If the statement is false, write the correction for the underlined words.

_____ 7. One theory suggests that <u>nomads</u> moved into the Indus Valley after 1500 BC.

_____ 8. The Aryans began a new period of civilization in the history of <u>China</u>.

_____ 9. Aryans spread across northern India and took control over the <u>Aryan</u> people.

_____10. The Aryans <u>settled</u> in the Indus Valley.

_____11. The <u>Indus River</u> nourished the Indus Valley that supported the Aryan cattle herds and farming.

_____12. A raja was the <u>least</u> important man in an Aryan village.

_____13. The rains come during the summer <u>dry</u> season in India.

Write _H_ if the statement describes the Harappan civilization or _A_ if the statement describes the Aryan civilization.

_____ 14. Their written language is called Sanskrit.

_____ 15. Horses pulled their light chariots with two spoked wheels.

_____ 16. They had well-organized cities.

_____ 17. These people were famous for their hymns, poetry, and prayers.

_____ 18. Their way of life became the characteristic culture of both ancient and modern India.

Etymology

_____

Refer to the Activity box on Student Text page 105. Complete the chart.

English word	Sanskrit word	English definition	Sanskrit definition
bandanna			
guru			
jungle			
loot			
mantra			
orange			
shawl			
sugar			
yoga			

Write a paragraph about your findings.

_____

_____

_____

_____

_____

_____

_____

_____

_____

_____

Hinduism

_____

Fill in the blanks.

1. The three gods that Hindus consider to be the most important are _____, _____, and _____.

2. The Rig-Veda is a collection of _____, _____, and _____.

3. The two basic groups in India since the rise of Hinduism have been the _____ and the _____.

Match each term with its correct description.

_____ 4. caste

_____ 5. karma

_____ 6. dharma

_____ 7. Vedas

_____ 8. Brahman

_____ 9. reincarnation

_____ 10. pantheism

_____ 11. Hinduism

_____ 12. untouchables

A The belief that after a person dies, he comes back in another form.

B The Hindu belief that a person's deeds, good or bad, determine his state in reincarnation.

C A strict social class a person is born into.

D Various groups of religion developed in India by the Aryans; includes Indian culture and beliefs.

E Collections of sacred hymn texts of Hinduism.

F Belief that everything in the universe is part of a supreme being.

G Religious duties of a Hindu or a Buddhist believer.

H Divine being of Hinduism believed to be the cause and material of creation; also called "the great soul" or "the world soul."

I A term previously used for an outcaste from Indian society; anyone from the lower castes; any Indian who is outside the caste system, who works with meat, or who has been expelled from his own caste.

Write the occupations for each level of the Indian social pyramid.

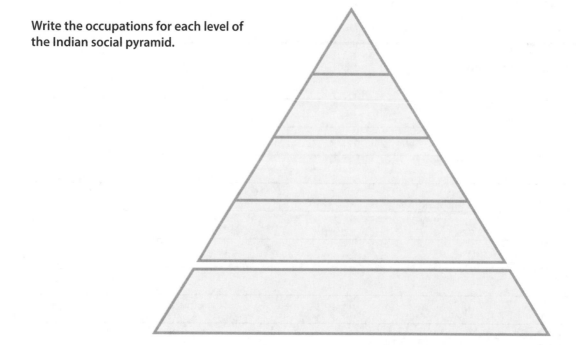

Identifying Cause and Effect

**Follow the steps to record five cause-and-effect relationships from Chapter 5.
The first two have been started for you.**

1. Choose an event or circumstance.

2. Decide whether it represents a cause or an effect.

3. Record it in the correct column in the chart below. If it is a cause, go to step 4. If it is an effect, skip to step 6.

4. Identify one of its effects. Think through these questions. What did this event lead to? What was the result? Look for clue words that signal an effect.

5. Record the effect in the chart below.

6. Identify the event or circumstance that caused it. Think through these questions. Why did this happen? What led to this? Look at the clue words for causes to help you.

7. Record the cause in the chart below.

Clue Words
Sometimes a writer will use words that signal a cause or an effect.
cause: as, basis, because, motivated, reason
effect: as a result, brought about, for that reason, led to, so, therefore

Cause	Effect
Because the Indus Valley was close to the river,	(page 100)
(page 103)	it is very difficult to crack the code.

Comparing Religions

Use the Student Text and the Bible to complete the chart.

	Hinduism	Buddhism	Christianity
Key person(s) or founder(s)	Varied groups of religions called Hinduism were developed by the _____. (page 106)	Buddhism was founded by a man named _____ _____. (page 112)	Christianity was founded by _____ _____, but it traces its roots back to the Creation.
God(s)	Hindus worship thousands of gods, but they consider _____, _____, and _____ the most important. The cause and the material of creation in Hindu beliefs is _____. (page 106)	There is no god in Buddhism. Some Buddhists believe that Buddha was a god.	The Bible teaches that there is _____ God in three Persons (Matthew 28:19).
Achievement of salvation	Hindus hope to be good enough to become one with Brahman by their religious duties, or _____. (page 106)	Suffering can be overcome by overcoming _____ that attach one to things in the world and by following the _____ _____. In Buddhism, the ultimate goal is to reach _____ with peace and freedom from desires and wants. (pages 112–13)	Salvation is received by trusting in _____, who paid the penalty for sin through His _____ and _____. Salvation results in good works (Ephesians 2:8–10; Philippians 3:9–10).
After death	Hindus believe in _____, the belief that after a person dies he comes back in another form. (page 107)	Buddha believed in _____. He believed that people would have another chance to reach nirvana. (page 113)	Whoever believes in Jesus' death and resurrection will one day be resurrected from the dead and have _____ life in heaven. (Romans 6:4–5)
Sacred writings	The sacred hymn texts of Hinduism are called the _____. (page 107)	A Buddhist's beliefs are found in the Pali Nikayas and other collections of Buddhist sayings.	The Bible is God's _____ (2 Timothy 3:16). It is divided into the _____ Testament and the _____ Testament.

Study Guide

_____

Match the description to the correct term.

_____ 1. a strict social class a person is born into

_____ 2. divine being of Hinduism believed to be the cause and material of creation; also called "the great soul" or "the world soul"

_____ 3. the Buddhist belief of a state of complete enlightenment where a person has peace and freedom from desire

_____ 4. the Hindu belief that a person's deeds, good or bad, determine his state in reincarnation

_____ 5. collections of sacred hymn texts of Hinduism

_____ 6. religious duties of a Hindu or a Buddhist

_____ 7. having received knowledge or understanding

_____ 8. the belief that after a person dies, he comes back in another form

_____ 9. belief that everything in the universe is part of a supreme being

_____ 10. a term previously used for an outcaste from Indian society; anyone from the lower castes; any Indian who is outside the caste system, who works with meat, or who has been expelled from his own caste

A	Brahman
B	caste
C	dharma
D	enlightened
E	karma
F	nirvana
G	pantheism
H	reincarnation
I	untouchable
J	Vedas

Write _True_ if the statement is true. If the statement is false, write the correction for the underlined words.

_____11. The Aryans developed a religion called <u>Buddhism</u>.

_____12. The hope of many <u>untouchables</u> was to do their duty, die, and have a better life in a reincarnated state.

_____13. The two basic social groups in Hinduism are the family and the <u>school</u>.

_____14. Siddhartha Gautama changed his name to <u>Asoka</u>.

_____15. Buddha's list of good works was the <u>Four Noble Truths</u>.

_____16. The <u>caste</u> dictated one's marriage, one's job, and one's clothing.

_____17. Siddhartha Gautama began the religion called <u>Hinduism</u>.

_____18. There were <u>five</u> main caste divisions in Indian society under Hinduism.

Complete the chart.

☸ Buddhism	✝ Biblical Truth
Buddhism teaches that the reason for suffering is _____ or _____ and that suffering can be avoided.	Suffering cannot be avoided because suffering is a result of _____ rather than just a result of desire.
Buddha teaches that in order to _____ suffering, a person must stop craving or desiring.	The goal of the Christian is _____ to escape suffering. The Christian endures suffering now as he looks forward to a _____ _____.

Study Guide

Plan the essay. Write the final draft on the lines provided.

25. Contrast Hinduism with biblical truth. Include three or more differences. _____

_____

_____

_____

_____

_____

_____

_____

_____

_____

_____

_____

_____

_____

_____

_____

_____

_____

_____

_____

_____

_____

_____

_____

_____

_____

_____

_____

Ancient India

Complete the organizer.

Organized Cities and Government
page 114

The first ruler of the Mauryan dynasty was

_____ _____. He chose

_____ as his capital and established a

_____ government there.

One of the greatest rulers of the Mauryan Empire

was _____, who united most of the

_____ _____ under

his leadership.

Religion
pages 114–15

Asoka worked to promote

_____ in his

empire. He built thousands

of dome-shaped shrines

called _____.

The Mauryan Empire

Job Specialization
pages 114–15

Chandragupta Maurya maintained an army of six hundred thousand

_____ and set up a network of _____.

Asoka had workers who _____ wells, _____

trees, and _____ hospitals throughout his realm. His most

well-known structure is the _____ _____. He

sent Buddhist _____ into areas outside his own borders.

India's Golden Age

The term *golden age* is used to describe the time when a country reaches its peak. India's golden age began during the rule of the Gupta dynasty under Chandragupta II. It lasted from about AD 320 to 550 and was a time of wealth, achievement, peace, and learning.

Education

A Hindu boy began his schooling at home, where he learned the alphabet and Sanskrit. Once he reached a certain age, his family held a special ceremony. A priest placed a sacred cord on the boy's left shoulder and fastened it under his right arm. The cord had three strands, each strand woven from nine threads. Throughout the rest of his life, the boy would wear the sacred cord as the symbol of his place in Hindu society. He then went to live with a *guru*, his teacher. The guru taught the Vedas and how to follow all the important Hindu rituals. Every activity, from cooking a meal to fighting a battle, followed a ritual to please the Hindu gods.

Number System

The Gupta age was the golden age of mathematics. Hindus invented Arabic numerals, which are the numerals used today. The people of India were one of the first cultures to use a zero. The zero invented in India spread into Europe in the 1400s. They also used the decimal system, place values, and positive and negative numbers. In advanced mathematics, the Indians learned how to find square and cubic roots, figured an accurate value for *pi*, and used elementary algebra.

Science

During the Gupta period, scholars studied chemistry, physics, and astronomy. They described the principle of gravity. They even had an idea of how atoms make up all matter. Indian astronomers discovered that the earth and all the planets are spheres and that the earth rotates.

Art

The art of this period appeared peaceful and happy. The wealthy enjoyed painting. Most gentlemen and ladies knew how to paint. The best examples of known Gupta paintings are found in the caves at Ajanta. These paintings were done by Buddhist artists. Although the paintings primarily show scenes from the life of Buddha, they also depict how the people lived, what they wore, and what plants and animals they raised.

Music

Most music from this time was not written down. A performer began with a familiar tune and then improvised and made changes in the melody as he played. The main instrument that the Indians used was called a *vina*. The vina was a type of lute similar to a guitar. Other common instruments were flutes, drums, bells, cymbals, and gongs.

Literature

Many excellent writers lived during the golden age. Two popular types of literature were the fable and the fairy tale. Trade played a big part in spreading stories that Indian writers created, and fables and fairy tales were popular in other countries. Some familiar stories today are based on early Indian fables. One such story is that of Sinbad the Sailor from *One Thousand and One Nights*. Indian poetry was complex and did not spread like the fables. The ability to write poetry was very important. Competitions were often held to see who could write the best and most complicated poem.

Golden Age

Complete the puzzle.

Across

3. a boy's teacher
11. type of numerals used today
12. golden age of ___
13. a sacred ___ worn by a boy to show his place in society
15. a ___ for every activity
16. ruler of the Gupta dynasty
17. writings taught by the guru
18. location of caves with wall art
19. story of ___ the Sailor

Down

1. art form that was improvised
2. dynasty name of the golden age
4. a popular type of literature
5. the main musical instrument
6. one of the first civilizations to use ___
7. men who discovered that the earth rotates
8. language learned at school
9. rituals to please the ___ gods
10. main subject of cave paintings
14. scientific principle described by scholars

Study Guide

Write the correct term to complete each statement.

1. Chandragupta Maurya _____ portions of India and became the first emperor of the _____.

2. Chandragupta chose _____ as his capital city and established a _____ government.

3. Asoka united most of the _____.

4. Asoka built thousands of dome-shaped shrines called _____.

5. Asoka improved the lives of his people since Buddhism emphasizes doing _____ and relieving _____.

6. Asoka spread _____ by sending _____ into areas outside his country.

7. Sir John Hubert Marshall was a British _____ who restored the _____.

archaeologist
Buddhism
centralized
conquered
good works
Great Stupa
Indian subcontinent
Mauryan Empire
missionaries
Pataliputra
stupas
suffering

Label the map.

8. Ganges River
9. Harappa
10. Himalaya Mountains
11. India
12. Indus River
13. Mohenjo-Daro
14. Pataliputra

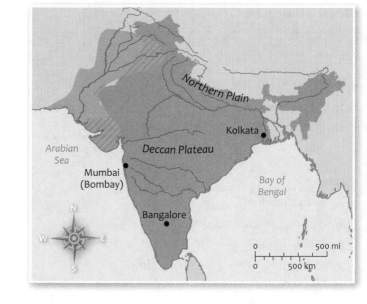

Complete the section.

15. Evaluate Chandragupta Maurya's rule. _____

_____

_____

_____

16. Evaluate Asoka's rule. _____

_____

_____

_____

Ancient China

Answer the questions.

1. What benefits did China's natural boundaries provide? _____

_____

2. How do the advanced skills of the ancient Chinese support biblical truth? _____

_____

3. What did the Chinese name their land? Why? _____

_____

4. How might the effect of geography be different for modern China than it was for ancient China?

_____

_____

_____

Fill in the blanks.

5. China is the _____-largest country in the world today.

6. China is located in East Asia, also known as the _____.

7. Modern China shares its borders with _____ countries.

8. China has a climate that is affected by yearly _____.

9. Modern China is one of the world's largest producers of _____ _____.

10. The highest mountains in the world are the _____ _____.

11. The Gobi Desert and the Taklamakan Desert are dangerous because of _____

_____ and _____ _____.

12. The Pacific Ocean isolated ancient China because few civilizations had mastered _____.

Match the region of China with its topography.

> **A** some of the highest mountain peaks
> **B** hilly and mountainous
> **C** lowlands
> **D** rolling hills

_____ 13. eastern region

_____ 14. central region

_____ 15. western region

_____ 16. southwest region

Ancient China

Complete the fishbone organizer as you read about the Shang dynasty.

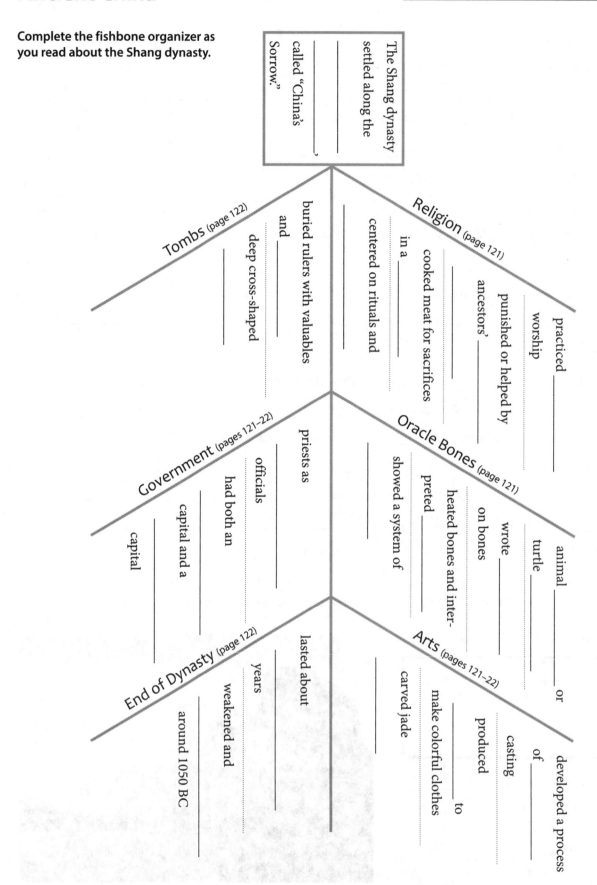

The Shang dynasty settled along the _____ called "China's Sorrow."

Religion (page 121)
- practiced _____ worship
- punished or helped by ancestors' _____
- cooked meat for sacrifices in a _____
- centered on rituals and _____

Tombs (page 122)
- buried rulers with valuables and _____
- deep cross-shaped _____

Oracle Bones (page 121)
- animal _____ or turtle _____
- wrote _____ on bones
- heated bones and interpreted _____
- showed a system of _____

Government (pages 121–22)
- priests as _____ officials
- had both an _____ capital and a _____ capital

Arts (pages 121–22)
- developed a process of _____ casting
- produced _____ to make colorful clothes
- carved jade _____

End of Dynasty (page 122)
- lasted about _____ years
- weakened and _____ around 1050 BC

Study Guide

Define the terms using the glossary and Student Text pages.

1. ting _____

   _____

2. oracle bones _____

   _____

Complete the chart.

3–6. Contrast ancestor worship with biblical truth.

⚬ Ancestor Worship	✝ Biblical Truth
The Chinese believed _____ had power to influence the _____ of the _____ .	The Bible teaches that only God _____ all things. Daniel 4:34 says that God's "_____ is an everlasting _____ ."
Many Chinese still believe that descendants must perform _____ to give ancestors the proper _____ . These rites show honor to the _____ .	The Bible teaches that children should honor _____ (Exodus 20:12), but Luke 14:26 teaches that honoring parents must not be placed above honoring _____ .

Complete the statements.

7. The Huang He was called "China's Sorrow" because _____

   _____

8. The Chinese people were protected from foreign invaders by the natural boundaries of _____

   _____

9. The Chinese named their land the Middle Kingdom because _____

   _____

10. The oracle bones show that the Shang had a system of _____

11. The Shang made advances in other arts, but are best known for their works of _____

12. Farmers produced silk, which weavers made into colorful _____

13. The discovery of the royal tombs at Anyang was important because _____

   _____

Ancient China

Complete the fishbone organizer as you read about the Zhou dynasty.

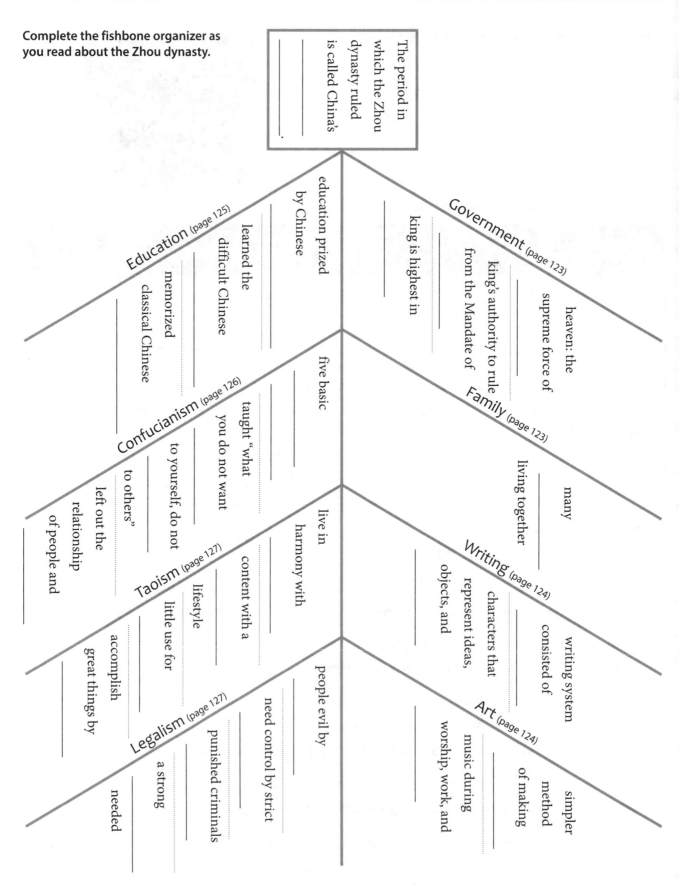

The period in which the Zhou dynasty ruled is called China's _____ _____ _____.

Government (page 123)

heaven: the supreme force of _____

king's authority to rule from the Mandate of _____

king is highest in _____

Education (page 125)

education prized by Chinese

learned the difficult Chinese _____

memorized classical Chinese _____

Confucianism (page 126)

five basic _____

taught "what you do not want _____ to yourself, do not _____ to others"

left out the relationship of people and _____

Family (page 123)

many _____ living together

Writing (page 124)

writing system consisted of _____

characters that represent ideas, objects, and _____

Taoism (page 127)

live in harmony with _____

content with a _____ lifestyle

little use for _____

accomplish great things by _____

Art (page 124)

simpler method of making _____

music during worship, work, and _____

Legalism (page 127)

people evil by _____

need control by strict _____

punished criminals _____

a strong _____ needed

Ancient China

Define the terms using the glossary and Student Text pages.

1. philosopher _____

2. proverb _____

Answer the questions.

3. How was the making of bronze in the Zhou dynasty different from bronze crafting in the Shang dynasty?

_____

4. How was the use of bronze similar in both the Zhou and Shang dynasties? _____

_____

5. What books are considered the classics of Chinese literature? _____

_____

6. What proverb expresses Confucius's belief about human relationships? _____

_____

7. Read Luke 6:31. How does the proverb in the previous question compare to this Bible verse? _____

_____

Write _True_ if the statement is true. If the statement is false, write the correction for the underlined word.

_____ 8. Education was <u>important</u> during the Zhou Dynasty.

_____ 9. Confucius wrote many proverbs about <u>religious</u> life.

_____ 10. Confucius made education available to <u>all</u> social classes.

_____ 11. Students spent many years learning the <u>easy</u> Chinese language.

_____ 12. Throughout much of Chinese history, no one exceeded the influence of the <u>kings</u>.

_____ 13. Confucius taught that proper <u>behavior</u> would allow people to live in happiness.

_____ 14. Confucius believed in <u>four</u> basic human relationships.

_____ 15. Confucianism leaves out the most important relationship of all: people and <u>God</u>.

Comparing Religions

_____

Use the Student Text and the Bible to complete the charts.

Confucianism (page 126)	Christianity
Confucianism identifies _____ basic _____ relationships.	The Bible teaches that the most important relationship is between _____ and _____. (page 126)
Confucius knew that it was impossible for people to always _____ other people as they would want to be _____. He told his followers to simply do their _____.	The Bible teaches that trying one's _____ is not _____ enough. God is a _____ judge who must judge _____. A person can be declared right with God only through _____. (page 126)
Confucius did not think there was a _____ who would judge all people.	The Bible teaches that there is _____. (1 Corinthians 8:6)

Taoism (page 127)	Christianity
Taoism teaches that true philosophy does not depend on _____.	The Bible uses words to describe _____ God is, to tell of the problem of _____, and to tell how the Son of God became a _____, lived, and died to _____ people from their _____. (page 127)
Taoism teaches that people should not seek power, _____, or _____.	The Bible teaches that people should _____ to show themselves approved (2 Timothy 2:15), and it is not money but the _____ of money that is condemned. (1 Timothy 6:10)
Taoism teaches that people should be content with a _____ lifestyle and live together in _____ and _____.	The Bible teaches that people should love their _____ as themselves (Mark 12:31), but the first commandment is to love the _____. (Mark 12:30)
Taoism teaches that people should find peace by living in harmony with _____.	The Bible teaches that Jesus made peace through the _____ of His _____. (Colossians 1:20)

Study Guide

Match the terms with the correct definitions.

_____ 1. classical age

_____ 2. Mandate of Heaven

_____ 3. philosopher

_____ 4. proverb

> **A** a wise saying that expresses a simple truth
> **B** a time of cultural development and achievement in a civilization
> **C** a scholar who dedicates himself to the pursuit of earthly wisdom
> **D** a belief that heaven gave the king his right to rule

Complete the sentences to identify the cultural aspects and achievements that made the Zhou dynasty China's classical age.

5. China developed and preserved its culture by establishing strong _____.

6. The family included many _____ that lived together.

7. The Chinese established a _____ system.

8. Chinese writing became a form of _____.

9. The Zhou developed a simpler method of

    _____ _____.

10. Music was played during times of _____,

    _____, and _____.

11. A good education was highly prized by Chinese

    _____.

12. Scholars wrote many books that are considered the

    _____ of Chinese literature.

13. Students learned the difficult Chinese _____ and memorized classical Chinese

    _____.

Name the philosophy.

_____ 14. The people of a nation would be good only if the government set the right example of goodness.

_____ 15. People should live in harmony with nature.

Complete the section.

16. What did the Zhou leaders believe justified their rebellion against the Shang? _____

    _____

17. List the two duties that Confucius taught as part of the five basic relationships. _____

    _____

Study Guide

Match the philosophies with their teachings.

_____ 18. If proper relationships in five areas are kept, society will have harmony and order.

_____ 19. People are evil by nature and should be controlled by strict laws.

_____ 20. People can find peace and happiness by living in harmony with nature.

_____ 21. A strong ruler is needed to maintain order.

_____ 22. People should be content with a simple lifestyle.

_____ 23. "What you do not want done to yourself, do not do to others."

C	Confucianism
T	Taoism
L	Legalism

Complete the T-chart.

24–25. Contrast Confucianism and Taoism. List two differences.

Confucianism	Taoism

First, plan the essay on your own paper. Then write it below.

26. Compare and contrast Confucianism with biblical truth. Include at least three points.

_____

_____

_____

_____

_____

_____

_____

_____

_____

_____

_____

Ancient China

Complete the fishbone organizer as you read about the Qin dynasty.

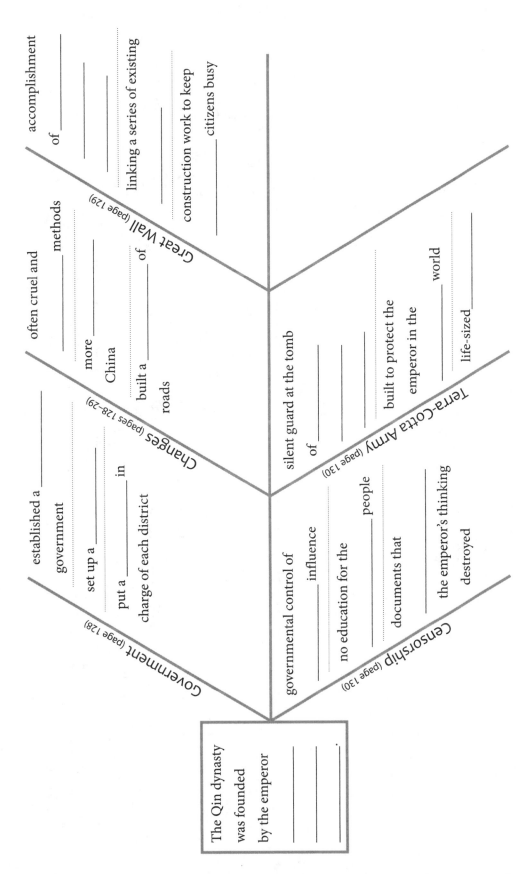

Great Wall (page 129)
- accomplishment of _____
- linking a series of existing _____
- construction work to keep _____ citizens busy

Changes (pages 128–29)
- often cruel and _____ methods
- more _____ China
- built a _____ of roads

Government (page 128)
- established a _____ government
- set up a _____
- put a _____ in charge of each district

Terra-Cotta Army (page 130)
- silent guard at the tomb of _____
- built to protect the emperor in the _____ world
- _____ life-sized _____

Censorship (page 130)
- governmental control of _____ influence
- no education for the _____ people
- _____ documents that _____ the emperor's thinking destroyed

The Qin dynasty was founded by the emperor _____.

Ancient China

Complete the fishbone organizer as you read about the Han dynasty.

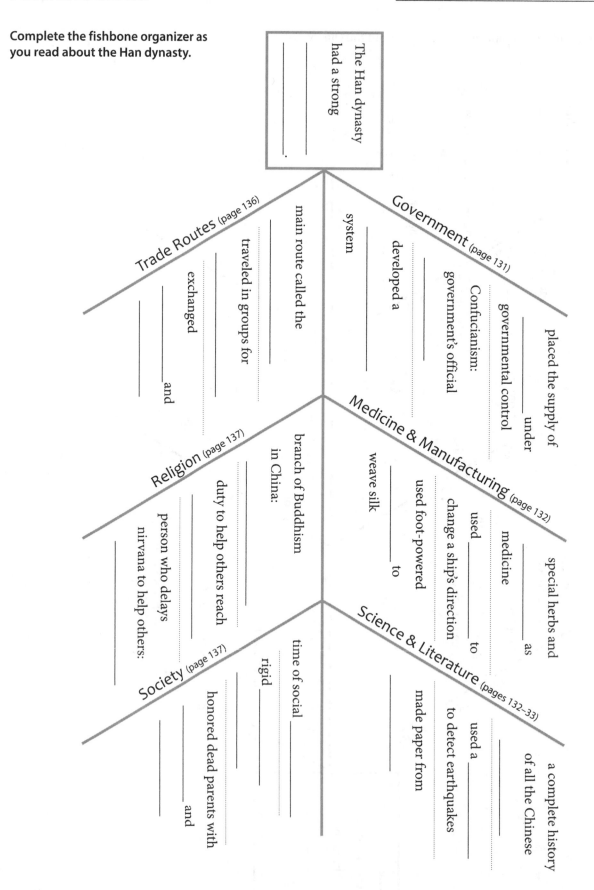

The Han dynasty had a strong _____ _____ _____.

Government (page 131)
- developed a _____ system
- Confucianism: government's official _____
- placed the supply of _____ under governmental control

Trade Routes (page 136)
- main route called the _____
- traveled in groups for _____
- exchanged _____ and _____

Medicine & Manufacturing (page 132)
- used _____ medicine
- used special herbs and _____ as _____
- used foot-powered _____ to weave silk

Religion (page 137)
- branch of Buddhism in China: _____
- duty to help others reach _____
- person who delays nirvana to help others: _____

Science & Literature (pages 132–33)
- used a _____ to detect earthquakes
- made paper from _____
- a complete history of all the Chinese _____

Society (page 137)
- time of social _____
- rigid _____
- honored dead parents with _____ and _____

Study Guide

_____

Match the description with the correct term. The terms may be used more than once.

_____ 1. was "First Emperor"

_____ 2. carved to protect Qin Shi Huang as he lived in the next world

_____ 3. buried alive or sent to work on the wall for not burning their books

_____ 4. disliked the teachings of Confucius

_____ 5. project that kept discontented citizens busy

_____ 6. lasting tribute to the Qin Dynasty

_____ 7. lifelike statues

_____ 8. standardized weights, measurements, and the money system

_____ 9. structure that kept out invaders from the north

_____ 10. one of the best-remembered accomplishments of Qin Shi Huang

_____ 11. persecuted by Qin Shi Huang because he thought they were breaking up his empire

_____ 12. were told not to waste time with education but to instead grow food

_____ 13. the managing of government through departments with appointed officials

_____ 14. established the same laws and taxes for everyone

_____ 15. feudal state that strengthened its military and began conquering neighboring states

A bureaucracy
B common people
C Great Wall
D Qin
E Qin Shi Huang
F scholars
G terra-cotta army
H the name *China*

Identify the places on the map.

16. _____

17. _____

18. _____

19. _____

20. _____

21. _____

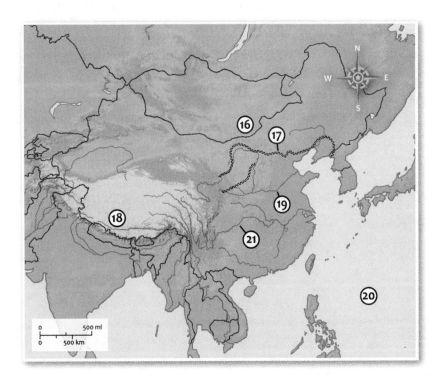

Study Guide

Match the description with the correct term. The terms may be used more than once.

_____ 22. invented the seismoscope

_____ 23. provided a strong central government

_____ 24. method to prevent or treat pain and sickness

_____ 25. poking needles into the skin at specific points on the body

_____ 26. expanded China's borders from North Korea to central Asia

_____ 27. detected earthquakes

_____ 28. made from hemp

A acupuncture
B bodhisattva
C Chang Heng
D paper
E seismoscope
F Silk Road
G Wu Ti

_____ 29. trained people for governmental service

_____ 30. use of the iron plow and wheelbarrow to increase production on farms

_____ 31. required a recommendation to begin

_____ 32. use of special herbs

_____ 33. swords and armor, which made the army more powerful

_____ 34. a complete history of China's dynasties through early Han

_____ 35. included three public exams

_____ 36. the rudder, which allowed ships to travel farther and establish trade connections

_____ 37. the seismoscope

_____ 38. acupuncture

_____ 39. foot-powered looms to weave silk

A civil-service system
B literary achievement
C manufacturing achievement
D medical achievement
E science achievement

China's Golden Age

For four hundred years after the Han dynasty, China suffered from internal wars and barbarian invasions. Then under the Tang and Song dynasties, the Chinese people enjoyed a time when their country was at its best. These six hundred years are called China's golden age (AD 618–1279).

Trade

During both of these dynasties, trade was an important part of China's economy. Through the Silk Road, the Chinese traded their famous silk, spices, and fine pottery. The Chinese not only traded their goods but also shared their ideas and inventions.

Literature and Poetry

All scholars had to be good writers of both poetry and prose. Their poems spoke of life, nature, home, friendship, and romance. Other golden-age literature included philosophy, religion, politics, stories, and fables. Writers produced many how-to books, giving instruction in painting, handwriting, and gardening. The Tang rulers began a tradition in which each new dynasty wrote the official history of the previous dynasty.

Printing

The Tang dynasty developed *block printing*. The printer carved a whole page of characters into a block of wood. The characters had to be backward, much like those on a rubber stamp. The oldest known printed book is a block-printed scroll dating back to AD 868. It is the *Diamond Sutra*, a book sacred to Buddhists.

The Song dynasty began to use movable-type printing. Each character was carved onto an individual wood block. The printer then arranged these characters to form a whole page. The major problem was organizing more than forty thousand characters of the written Chinese language.

Inventions

Chinese scholars put their minds to work on several other practical matters. Gunpowder was first used by the Chinese, but they did not use it in warfare until the Song dynasty. Earlier, they used it in firecrackers for social, religious, and victory celebrations.

The Chinese invented a way of making *porcelain*, a thin, but strong, translucent pottery. Porcelain, or "china," is made from a mixture of white clay and the mineral feldspar. Once the pottery dried, it was decorated with paint, carvings, or a glaze of liquid glass.

The Chinese produced other practical devices too. They discovered the magnetic compass and built highly accurate clocks run by water. The Chinese made rain and snow gauges that helped with flood control.

Architecture

The Chinese believed their buildings should blend into the landscape. Wooden pillars and beams supported the roofs of the houses, while the walls were simply screens decorated with carvings, paintings, or lacquer. Another Chinese building style begun during this age was the pagoda. Pagodas were first used as Buddhist temples. Soon, however, the pagoda was just another type of building used for many purposes.

Golden Age Puzzle

Complete the crossword puzzle using Activity Manual page 101.

Across

3. a building first used as a Buddhist temple
4. made sharing ideas and inventions possible (two words)
7. the second dynasty in the golden age
9. the first dynasty in the golden age
10. for example, the magnetic compass and rain and snow gauges
11. the position of the characters in block printing
12. for example, the pagoda and houses built with screens for walls

Down

1. a time when a country is at its best (two words)
2. what the Chinese clocks were run by
3. a thin, strong, translucent pottery
5. the oldest block-printed book (two words)
6. what the Chinese buildings blended into
8. used in religious and social celebrations before being used in war
11. the method of printing developed by the Tang

Study Guide

Match the description with the correct term. The terms may be used more than once.

_____ 1. a person who has reached enlightenment but delays nirvana to help others reach enlightenment

_____ 2. helped the exchange of ideas and inventions between countries

_____ 3. merchants needed armed guards to protect them from bandits here

_____ 4. sent his general, Zhang Qian, to explore regions west of China

_____ 5. the branch of Buddhism that spread to China

_____ 6. the main trade route between China and other regions

| A bodhisattva |
| B Mahayana |
| C Silk Road |
| D Wu Ti |

Plan the essay on a sheet of paper. Then write it below.

7. Contrast Mahayana Buddhism with biblical truth.

_____

_____

_____

_____

_____

_____

_____

_____

_____

Ancient Persia

_____

Refer to Student Text pages 140–42 to complete the page.

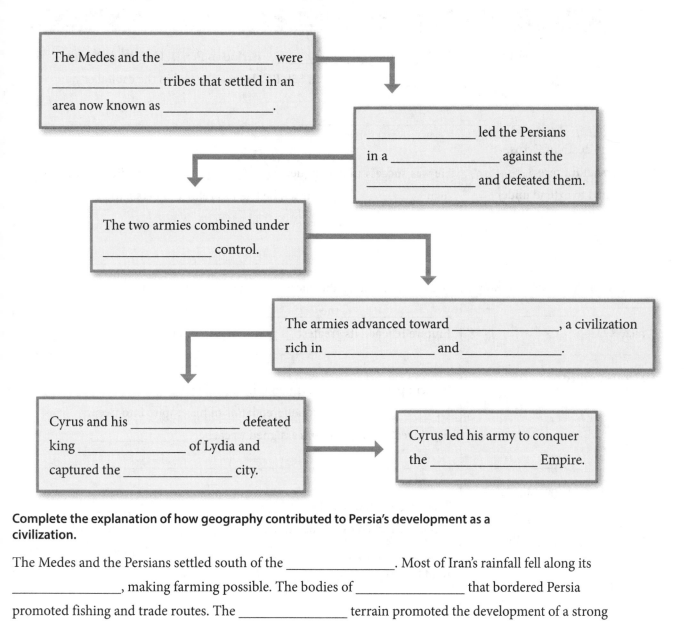

The Medes and the _____ were _____ tribes that settled in an area now known as _____.

_____ led the Persians in a _____ against the _____ and defeated them.

The two armies combined under _____ control.

The armies advanced toward _____, a civilization rich in _____ and _____.

Cyrus and his _____ defeated king _____ of Lydia and captured the _____ city.

Cyrus led his army to conquer the _____ Empire.

Complete the explanation of how geography contributed to Persia's development as a civilization.

The Medes and the Persians settled south of the _____. Most of Iran's rainfall fell along its _____, making farming possible. The bodies of _____ that bordered Persia promoted fishing and trade routes. The _____ terrain promoted the development of a strong _____.

Ancient Persia

_____

Complete each topic and its details.

Topic	Details
_____ began a dynasty in Persia. page 143	He began the _____ period in Persia. Cyrus ruled until his _____ in 530 BC. He was buried in the capital city, _____.
After the death of Cyrus, the Persian Empire continued to extend under _____. page 143	He was successful in conquering _____. He died by his own _____ when he tried to return to Persia to put down a _____.
After Cambyses, the next king was _____. page 143	Because of his long and successful reign, he was known as _____ the _____. Under his rule, the Persian Empire reached its greatest _____ and _____.
Darius formed a _____ government. page 143	He set up a place for government in one central _____. He _____ conquered lands of his empire into twenty provinces. A governor was assigned to each _____.
Darius built 8,000 miles of stone _____ to _____ the kingdom. page 144	The longest road was the _____ _____, which stretched over 1,600 miles from _____ to Sardis. _____ _____ were stationed along this road to carry messages _____ style.

Ancient Persia

_____

Complete each topic and its details.

Topic	Details
The road system helped long-distance _____ to flourish in Persia. page 145	The expanded empire gave access to new _____ and more ports for trade. The demand for goods grew as people saw the _____ of goods that were carried on the Persian _____. Darius introduced common _____, such as the _____ and the shekel, that was used as an _____ means of trade.
Herodotus was known as the _____ of _____. page 145	He recorded major events of his time in _The_ _____. Much of what people know about ancient _____ comes from his _____. He recorded backgrounds and _____ of foreign people he came in contact with during his _____.
Darius had a strong force of trained _____ to keep his empire under control. page 146	He had his own special force of ten thousand soldiers called the _____. Persia had a _____ that led an attack and was followed by _____ soldiers. Darius used his army to end _____ during his reign. He also used the army to _____ his empire.

Ancient Persia

Refer to the maps on pages 140 and 144 to complete the page.

Color the map to show the extent of the Persian Empire under Cyrus's rule.

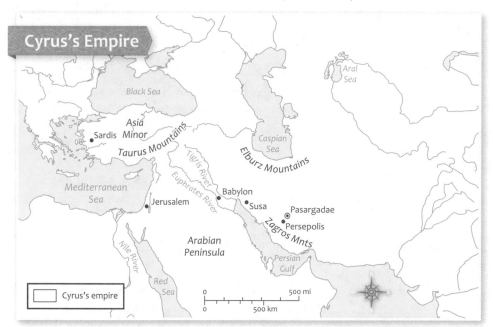

Color the map to show the extent of the Persian Empire under Darius's rule.

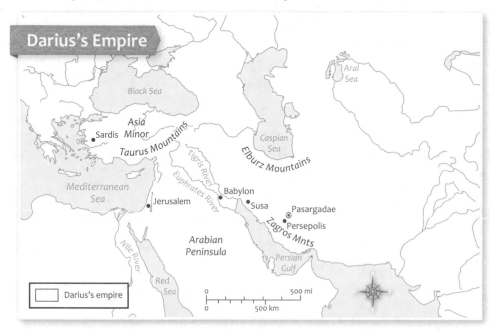

Compare the maps to answer the questions.

1. Did Cyrus or Darius have the largest empire? _____

2. What northwestern country did Darius conquer that was not part of Cyrus's empire? _____

3. What territory to the southwest did Darius add to his empire? _____

Study Guide

_____

Number the events in correct order.

_____ The armies advanced toward Lydia, a civilization rich in silver and gold.

_____ Cyrus led his army to conquer the Babylonian Empire.

_____ The two armies combined under Persia's control.

_____ The Medes and the Persians settled in an area now known as Iran.

_____ Cyrus and his armies defeated King Croesus of Lydia and captured the capital city.

_____ Cyrus II led the Persians in a rebellion against the Medes and defeated them.

Mark all the correct answers.

7. Some ways geography contributed to the development of the Persian civilization include that

   ○ there was access to bodies of water for fishing and trade routes.

   ○ there were coastal plains that supported crops and livestock.

   ○ mountains were barriers and promoted the development of a cavalry.

8. The first rulers of Persia during the Achaemenid period were

   ○ Cambyses, Herodotus, and Cyrus.

   ○ Cyrus, Croesus, and Darius.

   ○ Cyrus, Cambyses, and Darius.

9. A comparison of Cyrus's empire and Darius's empire shows

   ○ that both empires were the same size.

   ○ part of Egypt was in Darius's empire but not Cyrus's empire.

   ○ part of Greece was in Darius's empire but not Cyrus's empire.

10. Trade flourished in the Persian empire because

    ○ Darius introduced a common currency.

    ○ Persian roads allowed for international trade.

    ○ the demand for goods grew as people saw a variety of products carried on the roads.

11. Darius managed his expanded empire

    ○ by developing a central government.

    ○ by building roads to connect the empire.

    ○ without maintaining a strong well-trained military.

12. Herodotus

    ○ was known as the Father of History and spent most of his adult life working on *The Histories*.

    ○ provided much information about ancient Persia in his writings.

    ○ recorded backgrounds and customs of foreign people he came in contact with during his travels.

Study Guide

_____

First, plan your essay in the space below. Then, write your essay on the lines.

13. Explain the role of Darius in the restoration of the temple.

_____

_____

_____

_____

_____

_____

_____

_____

_____

_____

Ancient Persia

Refer to Student Text page 151 to compare and contrast Zoroastrianism and Christianity.

⚜ Zoroastrianism	✝ Biblical Truth
There are two _____ beings.	The Bible does not teach that Satan is an _____ spirit. God is the only _____ being.
The entirely _____ spirit is Ahura Mazda, and the entirely _____ spirit is Angra Mainyu who are _____ in power and are in a _____ against each other.	The Bible also teaches there is a _____ between good and evil, but it does _____ teach that God and Satan are _____.
If the good deeds _____ the evil, that person crosses the bridge and ascends to _____. If the evil deeds outweigh the _____, the person plunges off the bridge into _____.	People will not be _____ by whether their good works outweigh their bad works. They will be judged on whether they have _____ Jesus to be their _____.
In the last day, both the good and the evil will be _____ to pass through a last _____ by fire.	The Bible teaches that there will be a _____ judgment when people are _____ from the dead and _____.
The wicked will be consumed by the _____. The good will become _____ and will live _____ with Ahura Mazda in a garden paradise.	The Bible teaches that people must have the _____ of Christ credited to them to have _____ life.

Ancient Persia

_____

Complete the chart about Persia's wars with Greece.

Topic	Details
How the war began page 152	Greek city-states in Asia Minor _____ against the Persians. Athens and other city-states sent an _____ to help the Greeks in Asia Minor. Persia put down the _____. Darius sailed to the plain of _____.
Battle of Marathon page 152	An Athenian general ordered his men to _____ the Persians. He placed the army in a _____ _____ and had his soldiers _____ full speed toward the Persians. When the _____ of the line of Greek soldiers was pushed back by the Persians, the soldiers on the ends of the line _____ both sides of the Persian army, trapping them. The _____ lost the battle.
Battle of Thermopylae page 153	The Greeks positioned their forces at a mountain _____ called Thermopylae. They hoped to defend the pass and hold back the _____ army. A Greek _____ showed the Persian army another way through the _____. The Persians _____ the Greek army and _____ them.
Battle of Salamis page 154	The Greeks lured the Persians into the strait between the island of _____ and mainland _____. Greek _____ launched from the beach of Salamis. The Greek ships _____ and _____ many Persian ships. The Greeks _____ the battle.
Battle at Plataea page 154	Persia had to admit _____ after many Persian soldiers were _____. Xerxes pulled out the remaining Persian troops and _____ _____.

Study Guide

_____

Complete the section.

1. Write the name of the language spoken in ancient Persia by the common people. _____

2. Write the name of the language spoken by Persian kings. _____

3. What was the significance of the Behistun carvings in deciphering ancient cuneiform?

    _____

    _____

    _____

    _____

4. What can be inferred about ancient Persia from its art? _____

    _____

    _____

    _____

    _____

    _____

First, plan your essay in the space below. Then, write your essay on the lines.

5–8. Compare and contrast Zoroastrianism with biblical truth.

    _____

    _____

    _____

    _____

    _____

    _____

    _____

    _____

Study Guide

Write the correct name or term next to each clue.

_____ 9. A rebellion broke out here because Persia wanted to expand its borders into mainland Greece.

_____ 10. This man became furious when Athens and other city-states banded together to help in the rebellion.

_____ 11. The Persian king and his army sailed to this plain near Athens.

_____ 12. These people created a battle strategy that closed in on the enemy like pincers.

_____ 13. According to this, a runner named Pheidippides ran more than 25 miles to Athens to report the victory.

_____ 14. This man continued the war with Greece after Darius's death.

_____ 15. The Persian army passed over this strait on its way to Greece.

_____ 16. The Greeks hoped to defend this pass and hold back the Persian army.

_____ 17. This army was victorious after a traitor showed them another way through the mountains to the pass.

_____ 18. This Athenian general had a plan to win the war with Persia.

_____ 19. The Greeks won this battle by ramming and sinking Persian ships.

_____ 20. The Persian Empire had to admit defeat after many soldiers were killed at the battle at this city.

Study Guide

Refer to the map on Student Text pages 152–53 to complete the map.

21. Draw in green the sea route Darius's navy sailed.

22. Draw in red the land route Xerxes's army traveled.

23. Trace in blue the route that Xerxes's navy sailed.

24. Label the Hellespont.

25. Circle the locations of the battles that Persia fought with Greece.

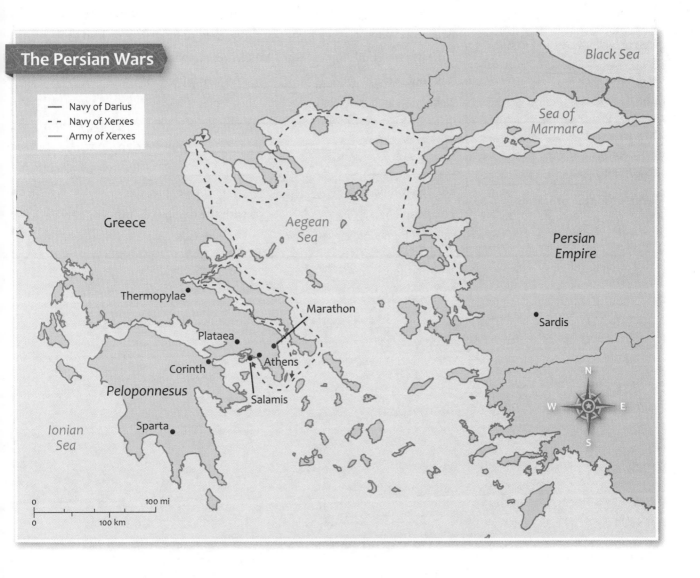

Ancient Persia

Refer to Student Text page 155 to complete the chart about the decline of the Persian Empire.

Main Idea	Details
_____ was the last of the strong Achaemenid kings.	He continued the _____ projects of his ancestors. He also dealt with a major _____ revolt and skirmishes with the _____.
Artaxerxes was kind to the _____.	He paid _____ expenses to travel to Jerusalem to teach the Israelites. When _____ returned to Jerusalem to lead the Israelites in rebuilding the wall, Artaxerxes supplied _____ for building the city _____ and sent letters to _____ Nehemiah as he traveled.
Persia had _____ since the rule of Darius I.	The wars with Greece were _____. But Persian _____ continued their _____ lifestyle by placing heavier and heavier _____ on the people. The people were _____ with the high taxes and with their rulers. The people's _____ decreased.

Ancient Persia

_____

Refer to Student Text page 156 to complete the chart about the decline of the Persian Empire.

Main Idea	Details
In 334 BC, _____ invaded the Persian Empire.	He _____ the Persians, and within four years, Alexander _____ all the lands of the former Persian Empire. Alexander _____ Persepolis, destroying many of its beautiful _____ and works of _____. He continued the _____ government and placed the Persian _____ in his own army. He blended some Persian _____ with influences from _____ culture.
After Alexander's _____, four generals declared themselves _____ over parts of Alexander's empire.	Each general wanted to _____ the others and bring the kingdom under his own _____. _____ developed from the _____ of three of the generals. Greece and Macedonia were ruled by the _____. The _____ ruled Egypt. Syria and _____ were ruled by the _____.

Ancient Persia

_____

Refer to page 157 of the Student Text to complete the chart of how Persian rule was revived.

Main Idea	Details
The _____ defeated the Seleucid king and gained control of _____ territory again.	The Parni took over _____. During the reign of Mithradates and Artabanus II, the _____ extended their control. They _____ nearly all the _____ part of the former Persian Empire.
Parthian rule lasted about _____ _____.	Parthians had close contact with the _____ as shown in their _____ and the Greek writing on the _____ minted in Parthia. They also had contact with the _____ people farther east because the _____ _____ ran through their empire.
The Parthians were _____ by the Sassanians.	The Parthians lacked a strong central _____. They were weakened by _____ with the Romans before being defeated by the _____.

Ancient Persia

Refer to page 157 of the Student Text to complete the chart of how Persian rule was revived.

Main Idea	Details
The _____ Sassanian king defeated the _____ Parthian king and established himself as Persia's ruler.	The Sassanian kings wanted to _____ _____ all that was truly Persian and to _____ the culture of _____ influences. Each ruler called himself a "_____ of _____." They ruled much the same as the _____ kings had. They _____ the central government again. They brought back _____ as the state religion. They had a strict system of _____ _____. Persia achieved its greatest _____ during this period due to _____ money and _____ from the Silk Road. There was a revival of Persian arts and crafts. Some Sassanian kings built _____, buildings, and _____. They improved irrigation and _____.
The Sassanians fought with the _____ and later the Byzantines.	Sassanian _____ from warfare brought decline, and the _____ of the ruling class waned.
_____ invaders conquered the last Sassanian king and introduced _____ to Persia.	The end of the Sassanian period brought an _____ to true Persian _____.

Study Guide

_____

Mark all the correct answers.

1. The Persian empire declined because

   ○ wars with Greece were costly and resulted in great losses.
   ○ Persian royalty continued their lavish lifestyle.
   ○ the people were discontent with the high taxes and with their rulers.

2. The book of Esther records that

   ○ the Persian king Xerxes took Esther to be his queen.
   ○ Esther approached the king's throne on behalf of the Jews without being summoned.
   ○ the king did not show favor to Esther and the Jews were not delivered.

3. Alexander the Great

   ○ was described in Daniel 8 through his rise to power, his conquest of Persia, and his death.
   ○ invaded and destroyed the Persian Empire.
   ○ destroyed the Persian form of centralized government.

4. After Alexander's death,

   ○ four generals declared themselves kings over parts of Alexander's empire.
   ○ dynasties developed from the families of three generals.
   ○ the Seleucids ruled Syria and Persia.

5. Persians controlled Persian territory again because

   ○ the Parni fought the Seleucid king and took Parthia.
   ○ the Parthians defeated the Sassanians.
   ○ the Parthians slowly extended their control.

6. The Sassanians

   ○ defeated the Parthians and began to rule Persia.
   ○ had kings that wanted to bring back all that was truly Persian.
   ○ had kings that ruled like the Achaemenid kings had.

7. During the Sassanian dynasty,

   ○ Persia suffered financial loss.
   ○ Persia achieved its greatest wealth.
   ○ Persia had some kings who built cities, buildings, and canals.

8. Persia declined under Sassanian rule because

   ○ it had losses from warfare.
   ○ the power of the ruling class grew.
   ○ invaders conquered the last Sassanian king.

9. Persian culture changed through the Parthian and Sassanid periods because

   ○ they were in close contact with the Greeks, as shown in Parthian art and coins.
   ○ of contact with the Asian peoples through the Silk Road.
   ○ Arab invaders conquered the Sassanians and introduced Islam to Persia.

Ancient Greece

_____

Compare and contrast the Minoan and Mycenaean civilizations by writing the correct descriptions under each civilization.

Minoans & Mycenaeans

Greece

Aegean Sea

Mycenae

Crete
Knossos

Minoans
ca. 2000–1400 BC

Mycenaeans
ca. 1250 BC

0   100 mi
0   100 km

instead of trading peacefully, they attacked cities and pirated ships

built large palaces that reflected a wealthy and artistic people

developed on the mainland of Greece

the civilization ended for unknown reasons

lived on the island of Crete

built large palaces that were heavily fortified

gained wealth from trading with other people

the civilization ended when invaders from the north conquered their fortresses

The Minoans	The Mycenaeans

Write the correct term to complete the description of Greece's geography.

Greece has various geographic features, including _____, valleys, natural

_____, and hundreds of tiny _____. It is a _____

bordered by seas, including the _____, the Mediterranean, and the

_____. The southern portion of the peninsula is called the _____.

Ancient Greece

Refer to the Student Text to complete the chart.

Athens pages 164–65	Sparta pages 168
People who had gained wealth and power were discontent with the _____. Some formed new ideas about what type of _____ was best.	Unlike _____, the Spartans _____ the oligarchy as their form of government.
In Athens, Solon wrote new laws allowing men of the _____ classes to take part in government.	Life in Sparta was much more _____ than life in Athens. The primary goal for young _____ was that they would become part of a strong _____. When a baby _____ was born, his parents _____ him to the rulers of the city. If the rulers of the city thought the baby was _____, he was allowed to _____. At age _____, a Spartan boy was taken by the army and trained to be a soldier. Around age _____, a Spartan man would _____, but he could not live at home with his wife. He lived with other men and _____ to be a soldier. The training was _____ and _____.
Men called _____ rose to power and ruled with _____ authority.	
Meetings of the _____ were open to all adult _____ citizens. Athenians voted on many things. Sometimes they voted by a show of _____. Sometimes black or white _____ were placed in an urn. When making a decision about ostracism, they wrote on _____.	
The Assembly met in the _____. This area also served as a _____.	
New _____ changed the government in Athens. It became a _____. The government was not always _____.	
The Greeks made _____ the leader of the democracy because they respected his _____ and his ability to _____.	Spartan women managed their _____. Spartan women had more _____ that Athenian women. They went out in _____ more often. Some women of Sparta owned _____. They received _____ training like the men.
Athenian women stayed at _____ most of the time. Women were skilled at _____ and _____. A few wealthy women learned to _____ and _____.	

Athenian Democracy

_____

Record the votes for each voting method. Complete a bar graph for each method.

1. Record the results for a vote by show of hands.

   yes votes _____   no votes _____

Vote by show of hands

   Number of votes

   30
   25
   20
   15
   10
   5

         Yes   No

2. Record the results for a vote by pebbles.

   yes votes _____   no votes _____

Vote by pebbles

   Number of votes

   30
   25
   20
   15
   10
   5

         Yes   No

3. Record the results for a vote by potsherds.

   yes votes _____   no votes _____

Vote by potsherds

   Number of votes

   30
   25
   20
   15
   10
   5

         Yes   No

Write a paragraph to answer the question.

4. Compare and contrast the methods of voting.

_____

_____

_____

_____

_____

_____

_____

_____

_____

Study Guide

_____

Write *True* if the statement is true. If the statement is false, write the correction for the underlined words.

_____ 1. The mainland of Greece is <u>an island</u>.

_____ 2. Landforms found in Greece include mostly <u>plains</u>, valleys, natural harbors, and islands.

_____ 3. <u>Crete</u> is part of Greece.

_____ 4. The Greek Empire covered much <u>less</u> area than modern-day Greece.

_____ 5. The <u>Mycenaeans</u> built large palaces that reflected wealthy and artistic people.

_____ 6. The <u>Minoans</u> gained wealth from trading with other people.

_____ 7. The <u>Minoan</u> civilization ended when invaders conquered their fortresses.

_____ 8. The <u>Mycenaeans</u> attacked cities and pirated ships.

Write *A* if the statement describes Athens or *S* if the statement describes Sparta.

_____ 9. Their government remained an oligarchy.

_____ 10. Tyrants rose to power and ruled with absolute authority.

_____ 11. Life was rigid in this city.

_____ 12. New laws created a democracy.

_____ 13. The women mostly stayed at home.

_____ 14. The primary goal for young men was to become a good soldier.

Complete the section.

15. What was unjust about the Athenian democracy? _____

_____

16. Who carried out justice in Athens? _____

_____

17. How were citizens treated justly in Athens? _____

_____

_____

18. What was unjust about the purpose of government in Sparta? _____

_____

_____

_____

_____

Study Guide

_____

19. What was just about life in Sparta? _____

_____

Use the map on page 161 in the Student Text to complete the section.

20. How does the landmass of ancient Greece compare to the landmass of modern-day Greece?

_____

_____

21. Compare the effects of geography on ancient Greece to its effects on modern-day Greece.

_____

_____

_____

_____

_____

Label the map.

22. Greece

23. Crete

24. Peloponnesus

25. Athens

26. Sparta

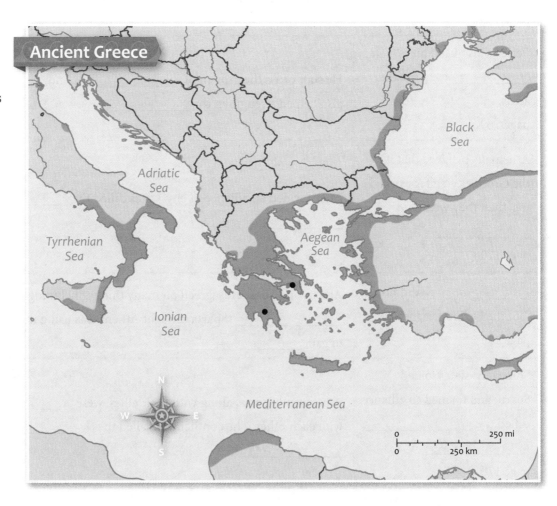

Ancient Greece

Ancient Greece

_____

Refer to the Student Text to complete the chart.

Main Idea	Details
The Greeks and the _____ fought in the fifth century. page 169	Persia wanted to _____ Greece and make it part of the Persian Empire. Athens won the Battle of _____. _____ joined the Athenian army to fight the Persians. Athens was _____ after the loss of the Battle of _____. Greece won the Battle of _____.
The _____ with Persia had taken their toll on Greece. page 169	Many _____ lay in ruins.
Pericles helped restore the former _____ of Athens. page 169	He encouraged the Athenians to rebuild the _____ and other sacred buildings on the _____.
Pericles also used his _____ in other areas. page 169	He supported the growth of _____ and _____. He also helped strengthen the _____.
Athenians believed that if the Greek city-states worked together, they would be _____. page 170	They formed an alliance of city-states called the _____ _____.
_____ did not join the Delian League. page 170	Athens and Sparta disagreed on many things, including their forms of _____. Sparta thought Athens was using the _____ to gain _____.
Some city-states joined Sparta and formed an alliance called the _____ _____. page 170	Athens and Sparta, along with their allies, were at _____ with each other. The conflict was called the _____ _____.

Ancient Greece

Refer to the Student Text to complete the chart.

Main Idea	Details
The Spartan army surrounded the city of _____. page 170	The Athenian navy supplied Athens with _____ and other items. A _____ broke out in Athens, and many Athenians _____. The Spartans left to avoid _____ the disease.
Athens made naval attacks on Sparta's _____ on the coast. pages 170–71	Athens and Sparta finally agreed to a _____. This agreement was broken when Athens attacked _____, an ally of Sparta.
Sparta won the war with _____. page 171	_____ defeated the Athenian fleet. Sparta joined forces with _____. The Spartan _____ took control of the _____. Athens was forced to _____.
Neither Sparta nor Athens ever fully _____ from the effects of the war. page 171	Both city-states had been _____ by their losses. Many people had _____. Buildings were in _____. _____ had been ravaged. Athens lost its _____. There was a time of _____ when Sparta lost control over the Greek city-states.
_____ was a historian who wrote about the Peloponnesian War. page 171	As an Athenian _____, he witnessed the war firsthand. His direct _____ and careful _____ were reflected in his writing. He recorded a _____ made by _____ at a funeral of a soldier who died in battle during the war.

Ancient Greece

_____

Refer to the Student Text to complete the chart.

Main Idea	Details
The Greeks believed in many _____. page 172	They believed the gods lived on _____ _____. The gods and goddesses were capable of _____ characteristics.
The Greeks' belief in many gods influenced Greek _____. page 172	Their drawings and _____ depicted gods and goddesses with human bodies. The Greek myths reveal how the _____ of the gods affected events in _____ or the lives of humans.
Scholars wanted to explain life by their own _____ rather than by the actions of the gods. page 174	These men were called _____.
_____ taught by asking his students thought-provoking questions. page 174	His questions made the students think about what they really _____.
_____ was one of Socrates's students. page 174	He wrote books called _____. He taught that a spiritual world of mind and ideas was _____ to the physical world.
_____ was Plato's pupil. page 175	He believed _____ was the most important academic subject. He used the _____ method of study. He taught that _____ controls _____.
Greek philosophers were right about some things, but they were _____ about many things as well. page 175	They emphasized virtues such as _____, love, _____, and discipline. The Bible teaches that virtues are gained only through a true knowledge of _____.

Study Guide

Mark all the correct answers.

1. Effects of the Persian Wars on the Greek civilization include that

   ○ many buildings lay in ruins.
   ○ Athens was burned.
   ○ manufacturing, trade, and the military were weakened.

2. Pericles helped restore the former beauty of Athens by

   ○ encouraging the rebuilding of the temple and sacred buildings on the Acropolis.
   ○ bringing in the classical age of architecture.
   ○ hiring unskilled architects, sculptors, and artists.

3. After the Persian Wars,

   ○ Athens and other city-states formed the Delian League.
   ○ Athens and Sparta formed an alliance which brought lasting peace.
   ○ Sparta and other city-states formed the Peloponnesian League.

4. During the Peloponnesian War,

   ○ the Spartan siege of Athens ended when a plague broke out.
   ○ the Spartan navy blocked the Hellespont.
   ○ Sparta surrendered to Athens.

5. The Peloponnesian War affected Greek civilization because

   ○ Sparta took control of Greece for about thirty years.
   ○ people lost their lives, buildings were destroyed, and farmland was ravaged.
   ○ Athens lost its democracy.

6. Thucydides

   ○ was a historian who witnessed the Peloponnesian War.
   ○ wrote from direct knowledge and careful research.
   ○ recorded one of Pericles's most famous speeches during the war.

Write *True* if the statement is true. If the statement is false, write the correction for the underlined words.

_____ 7. Fanciful stories about the gods are called <u>truths</u>.

_____ 8. The city of Athens is named after the Greek goddess <u>Artemis</u>.

_____ 9. Three major philosophers of Athens were Socrates, <u>Plato</u>, and Aristotle.

_____ 10. Greek philosophy included the idea that right thinking would lead to <u>wrong</u> actions.

_____ 11. <u>Socrates</u> was poisoned for causing young men to question belief in the gods.

_____ 12. <u>Aristotle</u> wrote books called dialogues that taught there was a spiritual world of the mind and ideas.

_____ 13. <u>Plato</u> developed the scientific method of careful observation and record keeping.

_____ 14. The Bible teaches that <u>virtues</u> are gained through knowledge of Jesus Christ.

_____ 15. Greek philosophers worshiped wisdom and reason, but the greatest human need is <u>redemption</u> through Jesus Christ.

First, plan your essay on a sheet of paper. Then, write your essay on the lines below.

16. Contrast the Greek religious beliefs with biblical truth.

_____

_____

_____

_____

_____

_____

_____

_____

_____

_____

_____

_____

Ancient Greece

Refer to the Student Text to complete the chart.

Topic	Details
Education page 176	Servants called _____ supervised the behavior of _____ boys attending school. Boys from _____ families could not afford to go to school. _____ were not allowed to go. Students wrote on wax-coated _____ with a _____.
Literature page 176	Literature included records of _____ or writings on _____. Stories were presented in _____ and drama.
Myths page 176	Greeks used myths to tell stories about _____ and _____. Some were about human _____. As storytellers passed down myths, sometimes new _____ of the myths were created.
Epics page 176	_____ created two long poems called *The Iliad* and *The Odyssey*.
Plays pages 177–78	Actors performed plays in _____ as part of _____ festivals. The two types of Greek drama are _____ and _____. The actors wore _____ to express the characters' feelings.
Fables page 178	Stories called fables were about _____ that talked and acted as humans do. Each fable usually ended in a _____. Many fables have been traditionally attributed to _____.

Ancient Greece

_____

ARCHIMEDES   EUCLID   PYTHAGORAS   ERATOSTHENES   ARISTARCHUS   HIPPOCRATES

Refer to the Student Text to complete the chart.

Topic	Details
Math and Science page 179	Pulleys were developed further by the mathematician _____. The first _____ book was written by a mathematician named _____. _____ studied geometry and developed a theorem about the area of _____. _____ was the first to draw lines of latitude and _____. He calculated the _____ of the earth. Aristarchus thought the _____ rotated around the _____. _____ contributed to the study of _____.
Athletics pages 179–80	Schoolboys exercised in the _____ by running, jumping, _____, boxing, and throwing the _____ and the _____. The Greeks were the first to hold the _____ games.
Music page 180	The Greeks believed _____ was the god of music. The word _music_ comes from the name for a group of nine _____ called _____. The Greeks believed that they presided over the _____ and the sciences.
Art and Architecture pages 180–81	The subjects of Greek art included _____ beings or _____ and goddesses. Sometimes _____ creatures or _____ were depicted. Greeks _____ their buildings by chiseling designs such as animals or gods into _____. They developed _____ to hold up buildings. The styles included the _____, the _____, and the _____. The _____ is the ultimate example of Greek architecture.

Ancient Greece

_____

Refer to Student Text page 182 to draw Alexander's route on the map.

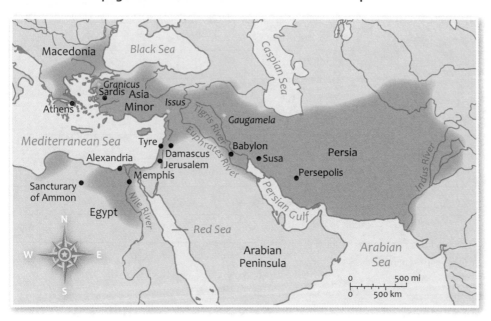

Write words to complete the answers to the questions.

1. What dream did Alexander pursue after taking control of the Greek army? He wanted to _____ the world under one _____.

2. What was the cultural impact of spreading the Greek Empire? The Greek culture _____ through _____ of the world.

3. What impact did the Greek culture have on the ancient world? People all over the Western _____ became _____. They _____ the ideas of Greek _____. They used Greek _____ and learned the _____ of Greek scholars. The works of Greek _____ appeared throughout the empire. A common _____ was brought to the Western world.

4. What resulted from Greek becoming the common language? Alexander made Greek the standard language of _____ and _____. Greek was the language of almost all _____ writing. The spread of the Greek language enabled the _____ to go into all the world when the _____ _____ was translated from _____ into Greek. The New Testament writers wrote in _____, giving many people access to the _____ of God.

5. How is the influence of the ancient Greeks seen today? Greek columns influenced _____ that decorate and _____ buildings today. Greek drama _____ to theater today. The _____ of sculpture and poetry is tied to the _____ that Greeks mastered. Greek discoveries influenced _____, _____, _____, and _____. The Greek _____ and writing skills allowed the New Testament to detail the _____ of the Lord Jesus Christ, who provides _____ for those who believe in Him.

Study Guide

_____

Complete the section.

1. Summarize education in ancient Greece. _____
   _____
   _____
   _____
   _____

2. Relate Homer's contribution to literature. _____
   _____
   _____
   _____

3. Describe each genre of Greek literature.

   myth— _____
   _____

   epics— _____

   plays— _____
   _____
   _____
   _____
   _____
   _____
   _____

   fables— _____
   _____
   _____

4. What were the achievements in math and science in ancient Greece? _____
   _____
   _____
   _____
   _____
   _____

Study Guide

5. Complete the table to compare and contrast athletic events in ancient Greece with modern-day Olympic games.

Compare and Contrast	Athletic Games in Ancient Greece	Modern-Day Olympics
How athletes prepare		
The events		
The prize		

6. List Greek achievements in the arts. _____

_____

_____

_____

_____

7. How did Alexander the Great spread Greek culture? _____

_____

_____

8. How did Greek culture affect the ancient world? _____

_____

_____

9. What contributions did ancient Greece make to modern times? _____

_____

_____

_____

_____

_____

Ancient Rome

_____

Complete the chart.

Topic	Details
Early Rome page 186	Settlers from central Europe sought _____ soil and a _____ that was suitable for farming. These people settled in the _____ Peninsula. They were called _____.
The founding of Rome page 186	One legend says that twin brothers named _____ and _____ founded Rome. They decided to build a city near the _____ River. The brothers quarreled, and _____ killed his brother. He built the city and named it _____.
Italy page 187	The Italian Peninsula and several islands, including _____ and _____, make up Italy. The mountains of the peninsula include the Apennine mountain range and sections of the _____. There are also broad _____. The _____ Sea, the Mediterranean Sea, and the _____ Sea surround Italy.
Etruscans page 188	Etruscans came from the _____ to conquer the Latins. Under Etruscan kings, Rome became the _____ and most respected city in the region. They paved _____, built arches, drained marshes, constructed a _____ system, and introduced a _____ system based on the _____ alphabet.
Society page 188	The Roman _____ included the mother and father, _____ daughters and sons, and married sons with their wives and _____. The _____ were the ruling class of wealthy landowners and nobles. The working class of farmers, traders, and craftsmen were the _____.
Early government page 188	The early government was a _____. The king was the chief _____, commander of the _____, and administrator of _____. The king's power was symbolized by the _____.

Read a Landform Map

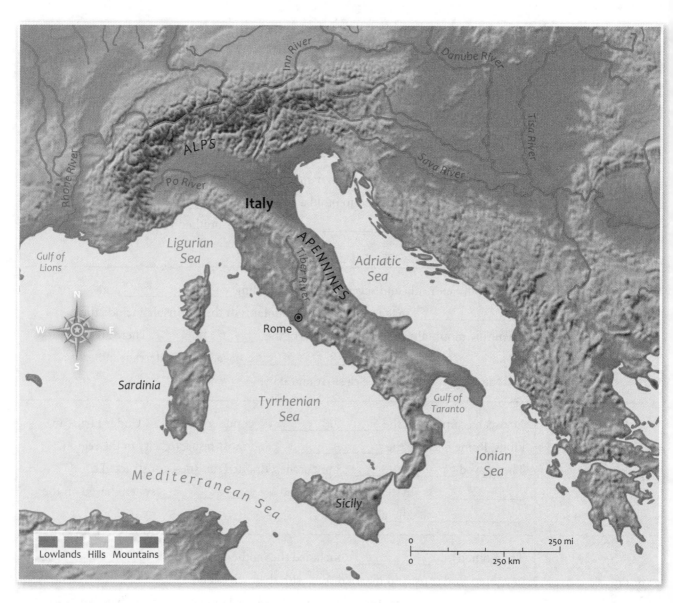

Answer the questions.

1. Where are Italy's mountains located? _____
   _____

2. What are the names of the two major mountain ranges in Italy? _____
   _____

3. Locate the Tiber River. What type of landform surrounds the river? _____

4. According to the map, lowlands are generally located along what geographical features? _____
   _____

5. Which landform was initially chosen to establish Rome? _____

6. What nearby landform promoted farming in the development of Roman civilization? _____

Ancient Rome

Complete the chart.

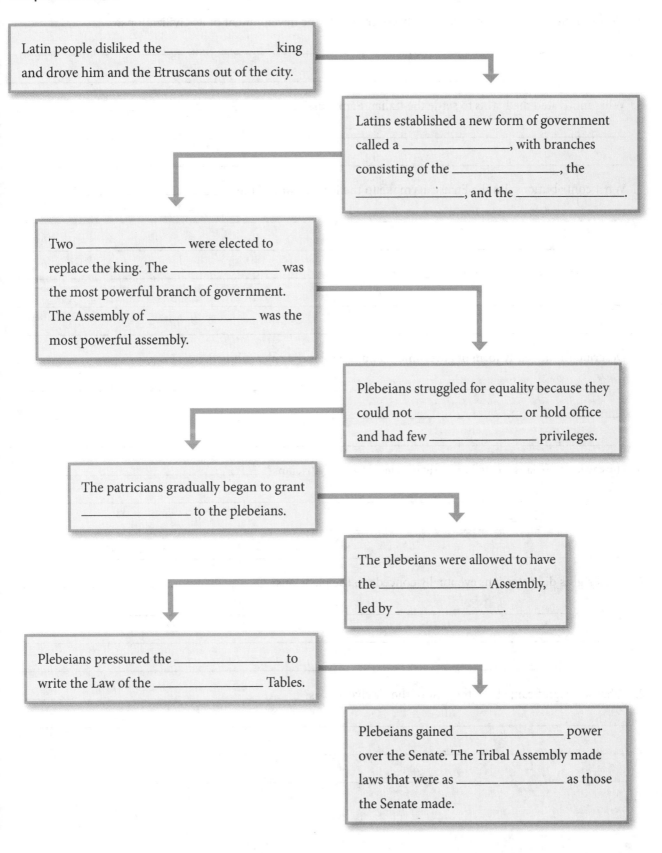

Latin people disliked the _____ king and drove him and the Etruscans out of the city.

Latins established a new form of government called a _____, with branches consisting of the _____, the _____, and the _____.

Two _____ were elected to replace the king. The _____ was the most powerful branch of government. The Assembly of _____ was the most powerful assembly.

Plebeians struggled for equality because they could not _____ or hold office and had few _____ privileges.

The patricians gradually began to grant _____ to the plebeians.

The plebeians were allowed to have the _____ Assembly, led by _____.

Plebeians pressured the _____ to write the Law of the _____ Tables.

Plebeians gained _____ power over the Senate. The Tribal Assembly made laws that were as _____ as those the Senate made.

Study Guide

_____

Complete the section.

1. How did the geographic features of Italy contribute to the development of its civilizations? _____

_____

_____

2. What motivated the Latins to settle the Italian Peninsula? _____

_____

_____

3. What contributions did the Etruscans make to the Roman way of life? _____

_____

_____

4. Describe the Roman social classes. _____

_____

_____

5. Describe Rome's early form of government and the roles the ruler fulfilled. _____

_____

_____

_____

6. How were plebeians treated unjustly in regard to the patricians? _____

_____

_____

_____

7. What rights did patricians eventually concede to the plebeians? _____

_____

_____

_____

8. What was significant about the Law of the Twelve Tables? _____

_____

_____

_____

Ancient Rome

_____

Use the Student Text to complete each section.

1. Use the description by Polybius on page 191 to compare and contrast Carthage and Rome.

Carthaginians	Romans
Carthaginians were more skilled in _____ _____, employed _____ mercenaries, and had great difficulty repairing their _____.	Romans were superior in the _____ and _____ of armies. The army was made up of _____ and people of that country. Romans placed their confidence in their _____ and help from _____. They easily _____ their armies when defeated. They had greater ardor, and they would _____ because they were fighting for their _____ and their _____. Romans often succeeded through _____ of their forces.

2. Refer to page 192 to explain the importance of the Roman roads.

   The Roman roads promoted _____ and _____ the lands Rome had _____. People _____ on these roads and exchanged _____ and ideas. Christians carried the _____ on the Roman roads.

3. Summarize the Punic Wars.

War	Details	
The First Punic War page 192	Rome and Carthage both wanted control of _____. Romans designed a ship with a plank that had a _____ tip. The plank could _____ to an enemy ship, allowing Roman soldiers to _____ and _____ the enemy. Using these ships, Rome was _____ over the Carthaginian _____. The two sides formed a _____ settlement. Rome gained _____ of Sicily.	

Ancient Rome

Complete the chart.

4. Summarize the Punic Wars.

War	Details
The Second Punic War pages 193–94	War began again when Carthage violated its _____ with Rome. _____ was a general of the Carthaginian army. He hoped to surprise the Romans by marching his soldiers across the _____. The cold weather made it difficult for the war _____ and Carthaginian _____. Mountain _____ attacked Hannibal's army. Many elephants and soldiers _____ in the cold Alps. Hannibal's army was _____ than the Roman army by the time he reached the _____ Peninsula. He won battles with Rome but could not completely _____ them. When a Roman army was sent to attack _____, Hannibal rushed back to protect his city. _____ won at the Battle of Zama.
The Third Punic War page 194	Carthage fought one of Rome's allies, which _____ the Romans. Rome _____ war on Carthage. Rome eventually captured and _____ Carthage, then _____ what remained of Alexander the Great's empire. They then conquered _____, made an alliance with _____, and gained control of the eastern Mediterranean world.

Third century silver coins. What do the images suggest about the importance of elephants to Carthage?

Ancient Rome

Complete the chart.

Topic	Details
Problems from Rome's expansion page 195	Farmers sold their farms _____ from neglect after returning from being soldiers. Many moved to the _____, only to find that many jobs had been filled by _____. The wealthy _____ from the wars by buying lands from conquered people and having slaves run the farms. The wealthy bought _____ in the Tribal Assembly to fill the government with more _____ men. In the provinces, many of the publicans and the government officials that they worked for became _____. They collected more _____ than needed and kept the extra money. Plebeians came to care only for what they could gain by _____ their votes.
Rivalry between commanders pages 195–96	The Senate appointed the general _____ to command the Roman army in the war in Asia Minor. The Tribal Assembly appointed _____ instead. _____ war erupted between the two commanders. After years of battles, Sulla and the Senate emerged _____.
The triumvirate page 196	_____, _____, and _____ _____ formed an alliance called a triumvirate to rule Rome together. _____ was appointed governor of Gaul. He trained an army and led many _____. _____ died in a war in Asia. _____ marched to Rome and fought a war against Pompey and the Senate. Caesar _____ Pompey's army. Caesar was proclaimed the _____ of Rome.

Ancient Rome

_____

Complete the chart.

Topic	Details
The Gregorian calendar page 197	The Gregorian calendar is based on the birth of _____, but it is similar to the _____ calendar. It adds an extra day to February every _____ years to create a _____ year that keeps the calendar up to date. The similarity to the Julian calendar is evident in the _____ of the months, many of which were based on Roman _____ or _____.
Death of a dictator page 198	Many Romans liked Caesar, but others were _____ with him. They knew that, as long as Caesar had _____ power, the government could no longer be a true _____. Brutus and _____ met with other senators and plotted to kill Caesar. On March 15, Caesar was _____. Octavian and Mark Antony formed an alliance and _____ the empire. Neither man wanted to _____ the power to rule Rome. Antony and Octavian fought a _____ battle off the coast of Greece. Octavian _____ Antony and became the ruler of the Roman world.

Study Guide

_____

Complete each section.

1–2. Use the description by Polybius to compare and contrast Carthage and Rome.

Carthaginians: _____

_____

_____

_____

Romans: _____

_____

_____

_____

3–5. Summarize each of the Punic Wars.

First Punic War: _____

_____

_____

_____

_____

_____

Second Punic War: _____

_____

_____

_____

_____

_____

Third Punic War: _____

_____

_____

_____

_____

_____

Study Guide

_____

Write the name of the place that corresponds to the number on the map.

6. _____

7. _____

8. _____

9. _____

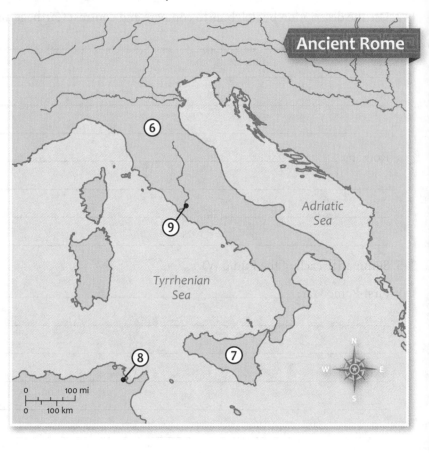

Ancient Rome

Adriatic Sea

Tyrrhenian Sea

0   100 mi

0   100 km

Write *True* if the statement is true. If the statement is false, write the correction for the underlined words.

_____ 10. Roman roads were used to promote trade, exchange cultural ideas, and carry the <u>gospel</u>.

_____ 11. <u>Farmers</u> returned from the wars to find their land ruined from neglect.

_____ 12. The <u>poor</u> profited from Rome's expansion.

_____ 13. Corruption in government led to <u>patricians</u> selling their votes and becoming less interested in government.

_____ 14. Crassus, Pompey, and <u>Hannibal</u> formed the triumvirate.

_____ 15. The Gregorian calendar adds a day to <u>June</u> every four years.

_____ 16. The Gregorian calendar is based on the birth of Christ and is an updated version of the <u>Julian</u> calendar.

Ancient Rome

_____

Complete each section.

1. What two main things characterized the Pax Romana? (page 199) _____

2. Complete the chart to contrast education in the Pax Romana (pages 199–200) with education today.

Education in the Pax Romana	Education Today
	Parents are responsible for educating their children.
	Some students study at home and are taught by a family member, but most children attend school.
	Children study the same subjects, plus others such as science, history, art, and music.
	Children write with pencils and paper or work on a computer. They calculate math problems on paper and sometimes use a modern calculator.
	Girls often receive training for an occupation by continuing their education. Many girls learn to work away from home.

3. Identify the main architectural feature of each. (page 201)

Colosseum: _____

Pantheon: _____

Relief of a teacher with three students during the Pax Romana AD 180–185.

Ancient Rome

_____

Complete each section.

Write words to complete the chart to contrast Epicureanism and Stoicism. (pages 204–5)

⚠ Epicureanism	🏛 Stoicism
Epicureans believed that the chief goal of life was _____. They believed that, by being free from _____, people can find true _____ in this life. They wanted to live happy lives, but they also wanted to keep their lives free from _____. They believed people should consider the _____ and avoid whatever would lead to pain instead of _____. God does give people pleasure, but the goal of life is not to avoid _____ and to maintain pleasure. The goal of life is to give glory and praise to _____. God did not intend people to be _____ of all fear. People should fear death and the _____ of God. The solution is to find _____ in Christ, who has taken that judgment in the place of _____.	Stoics believed that _____ governed all things, and they did not want people to _____ about things they could not control. They believed that doing one's _____ would lead to happiness. They emphasized _____, justice, and _____. Christians appreciate that the Stoics wanted to live a _____ life. Christians believe that people cannot become _____ by their own efforts. Christians believe that _____ brought things into the world that are truly bad. When Christ returns to _____ the earth, all things will be set _____. There will be judgment of the _____, and justice will be upheld.

Ancient Rome

_____

Complete the chart.

Topic	Details
Jesus Christ page 206	Jesus taught that people should _____ because the _____ of God is at hand. First, Jesus would suffer and _____ to pay the penalty for _____. His kingdom _____ as people follow Him, just as a small seed grows into a tall tree. Later, Jesus will come to _____ the world and set all things right. Christ's teachings angered _____ leaders, so they brought Jesus before _____. He found Jesus _____, but he had Jesus _____. At the feast of _____, Peter preached that God had _____ Jesus from the dead and that Jesus went up to _____ to _____. He preached that _____ should repent of their sins. About _____ thousand people repented and were _____, thus beginning the Christian _____.
Persecution page 207	The earliest persecution of the church came from _____. Romans sometimes _____ the Christians in order to preserve peace, until _____ blamed Christians for starting a fire that destroyed most of Rome. He ordered many Christians to be put to _____. Later, _____ was considered illegal. _____ during the second century was inconsistent. Christianity _____ despite the persecution it encountered.

Gold coin with the image of Nero and the Roman god Jupiter AD 54–68.

Study Guide

_____

Complete each statement.

1. _____ divided the empire in half, keeping the eastern part under his control. He appointed a ruler for the _____ half. His power was divided further by putting assistant _____ over each half of the empire.

2. The kingdom was weakened by the division over religious _____. Christians worshiped _____ rather than Roman gods. Diocletian persecuted _____. False _____ divided the church.

3. Soldiers gave allegiance to their _____ rather than to the empire. _____ tried to gain control of the government. There were financial _____ and _____ decay. Theodosius I _____ the empire between his two sons. The western part fell to _____.

4. Rome's decline in government, the economy, and society led to the _____ of the _____ _____.

Write _True_ if the statement is true. If the statement is false, write the correction for the underlined words.

_____ 5. Octavian's reign began a period of peace called the Pax <u>Republic</u>.

_____ 6. Romans used arches in the Colosseum and the <u>dome</u> in the Pantheon.

_____ 7. <u>Epicureans</u> believed that if people are free from fear, they can find true happiness in this life.

_____ 8. The Christian view is that the goal of life is to give glory and <u>praise</u> to God.

_____ 9. <u>Epicureanism</u> appealed to Roman soldiers because of the beliefs that doing one's duty led to happiness and that fate governed all things.

_____ 10. <u>Jesus</u> traveled throughout Galilee teaching and healing sicknesses among the people.

_____ 11. <u>Roman</u> leaders took Jesus before Pilate, insisting that the governor execute Jesus.

_____ 12. Three days after His crucifixion, Jesus <u>rose</u> from the dead.

_____ 13. About three thousand people repented and were baptized when <u>Moses</u> preached at Pentecost.

_____ 14. <u>Roman</u> roads enabled Christians to carry the gospel to many parts of the world.

_____ 15. <u>Nero</u> persecuted Christians by putting them to death.

The Byzantine Empire

Complete the organizer as you read about the birth of the Byzantine Empire.

The Village by the Sea (page 212)	
Byzantium was ideal for trading because it was . . .	close to the _____ Strait and had a _____ to the north. Villagers could travel through the _____ Sea and sail west into the _____ and _____ Seas.

The Birth of Eastern Power (pages 212, 214)	
Constantine chose Byzantium for his new capital because it was . . .	surrounded by _____ and high _____ on three sides.

The Rise of the Roman Church (page 214)	
Early believers faced persecution until the passing of . . .	the Edict of _____, which guaranteed freedom of _____ in the Roman Empire.
Some false teachers in the early church denied . . .	the _____ of Christ.
True believers in the church who defended the truth were called . . .	_____.
Constantine called the bishops of the church to a meeting that was called . . .	the _____ of _____.
The bishops tried to define what true Christians should believe about . . .	the _____.
What a certain group or church believes and teaches is known as . . .	_____.

The Byzantine Empire

_____

Complete the organizer as you read about the reign of Justinian.

Decline of the Western Roman Empire (page 215)	
Building a new capital away from Rome weakened . . .	the _____ part of the empire.
Theodosius I permanently divided the empire into . . .	the _____ Roman Empire and the _____ Roman Empire.
Several years after the division, Rome was plundered . . .	by _____.

Early Years of the Byzantine Empire (pages 215–21)	
The Eastern Roman Empire became known as . . .	the _____ Empire.
Justinian gave the job of conquering regions of the former Roman Empire to . . .	his general _____.
Justinian's army did not conquer all the former Roman Empire, but it did conquer . . .	_____ part it fought for.
Sporting and social events took place in . . .	open-air stadiums called _____.
Because of Justinian's high taxes and lack of respect for others' privileges, the people became . . .	increasingly _____.
Because of tensions over the punishment of men arrested after a riot, crowds moved through . . .	the streets, _____ and _____ buildings.
Justinian was convinced to stay and fight . . .	by his wife, _____.
The most famous structure built under Justinian was . . .	the church called the _____ _____.
Justinian had scholars write . . .	a new law code called the _____ _____.
Justinian's military campaigns and massive building program were . . .	extremely _____.

Political Cartoon

_____

Complete the cartoon analysis for one of the cartoons.

First Glance	
Visuals	**Words (Not all cartoons include words.)**
Objects or people	Caption or title
	Dialogue or labels
	Dates or numbers
A Closer Look	
Which objects are used as symbols?	Is the cartoon realistic or unrealistic?
What do the symbols represent, and why were they chosen?	Which words or numbers appear to be important? Why?
Is anything exaggerated? How?	List adjectives that describe emotions visible in the cartoon.
The Big Picture	
Describe the action taking place in the cartoon.	
Tell how the words in the cartoon explain the symbols.	
Identify the message of the cartoon.	
Identify groups of people who might agree and disagree with the cartoon.	

Study Guide

Match the term with its description.

_____ 1. barbarian

_____ 2. doctrine

_____ 3. hippodrome

_____ 4. orthodox

> **A** refers to those who support traditionally accepted principles of the faith
>
> **B** a belief or principle of a group of people
>
> **C** a nomadic person who did not speak Greek or Latin and did not adopt Roman culture
>
> **D** an open-air stadium for sporting and social events

Write _True_ if the statement is true. If the statement is false, write the correction for the underlined words.

_____ 5. Two challenges early Christians faced were <u>persecution</u> and false teachers.

_____ 6. At the Council of <u>Constantine</u>, the bishops tried to define what true Christians should believe about each person of the Trinity.

_____ 7. The Edict of Milan <u>denied</u> freedom of religion in the Roman Empire.

_____ 8. Moving the capital from Rome to Constantinople weakened the <u>western</u> part of the Roman Empire.

_____ 9. The division of the Roman Empire into separate parts made it <u>difficult</u> for barbarians to invade the Western Roman Empire.

Modern Istanbul's Galata Bridge spanning the Golden Horn inlet of the Bosporus. The Yeni Mosque is nearest the end of the bridge, and the Sultanahmet Mosque (the Blue Mosque) is in the background.

Write the correct name for each clue. Some names will be used more than once.

_____ 10. I conquered all the regions of the former Roman Empire that the emperor sent me to reclaim.

_____ 11. I moved the capital of the empire to Byzantium.

_____ 12. I kept the emperor from fleeing during the Nika Revolt.

_____ 13. As emperor, I had the code of Roman laws simplified.

_____ 14. I followed my wife's advice and did not run from the rioters.

_____ 15. With my men, I defended the emperor in the Hippodrome.

_____ 16. I gave good advice to the emperor on building projects and on running the government.

Study Guide

Complete the section.

17. What geographic features made Byzantium a strategic location for trade? _____

_____

18. What features protected Constantinople and made it a stronghold? _____

_____

Answer the questions.

19. Where did Belisarius go as he reconquered lands of the former Roman Empire? _____

_____

20. Why were people dissatisfied with Justinian's rule? _____

_____

21. Why did the nobles not rally to help defend Justinian? _____

_____

22. What does the word *nika* mean? _____

23. Why did Justinian want to simplify the laws of the former Roman Empire? _____

_____

24. Did Justinian rule well? Explain your answer. _____

_____

_____

Identify the numbered countries on the following map:

25. _____

26. _____

27. _____

28. _____

29. _____

30. _____

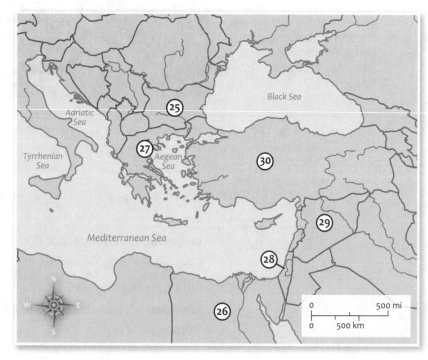

The Byzantine Empire

_____

Complete the organizer as you read about decline in the empire and the rule of Heraclius.

The Struggle for Existence (pages 222–23)	
The Byzantine army was made up of . . .	mercenaries, foreigners _____ to fight for a country.
The Persians attacked and took . . .	the province of _____.
The Avars and the Bulgars, barbarian tribes, conquered . . .	the _____ Peninsula.
The Lombards, another barbarian tribe, conquered . . .	the _____ Peninsula.
The emperor Heraclius reformed the army by firing . . .	the _____ soldiers and training peasant soldiers, whom he paid with _____ to support their families.
Heraclius organized the land by dividing it . . .	into provinces called _____.
Trade flourished and people formed . . .	groups with the same skills or occupations called _____.
Byzantine spies discovered the secret of . . .	making _____ and smuggled _____ back from China.
Heraclius changed the language of the empire from . . .	Latin to _____.

The Byzantine Empire

Complete the organizer as you read about the beginnings of Islam.

A New Religion (pages 224–26)	
A new belief formed on . . .	the _____ Peninsula.
Its contact with trade routes brought the city of Mecca . . .	great _____ and the rapid spread of _____.
The new belief was formed by . . .	a man named _____ who lived in Mecca.
Muhammad was interested in Christianity and Judaism because . . .	they were not _____.
At the age of forty, Muhammad claimed to receive a revelation from . . .	the angel _____.
Muhammad's revelations were put in a book . . .	called the _____.
Muhammad taught that there was only . . .	one god, called _____.
Muhammad and his followers traveled to . . .	_____ in 622 but returned to _____ by 630.
Muhammad's beliefs became the religion of . . .	_____, and its followers are called _____.
To conquer the entire Arabian Peninsula, the Muslim caliph Abu-Bakr led . . .	a _____, a holy war fought for the cause of Islam.
Umar won important victories against . . .	the _____ and the _____ Empires.
The three cities Muslims consider sacred are . . .	_____, _____, and _____.
The Islamic religion spread through . . .	military conquest and _____.
Besides their religious influence, Muslims made . . .	important _____ contributions.

Study Guide

Write the correct answer.

_____ 1. This man's teachings and beliefs developed into the religion of Islam.

_____ 2. This region between the Red Sea and the Persian Gulf was where Islam began.

_____ 3. A person who follows Islam is called this.

_____ 4. This is a holy war fought for the cause of Islam.

_____ 5. This type of soldier is a foreigner paid by the government.

_____ 6. The teachings of Muhammad were compiled by his followers into this book.

Complete the section.

7. How did financial and military weakness affect the Byzantine Empire after Justinian's death? _____

_____

8. Why was it difficult to keep the loyalty of conquered peoples? _____

_____

9. Why would mercenary soldiers make the Byzantine army weak? _____

_____

10. How did Heraclius strengthen the Byzantine army? _____

_____

11. How did Heraclius organize the empire's land and its defense? _____

_____

12. How did silk become a trade item for the Byzantine Empire? _____

_____

13. How did Muhammad's background influence his religious beliefs? _____

_____

14. Why did Muhammad and his followers leave Mecca in 622? _____

_____

15. What territory did Abu-Bakr and Umar add to the Islamic empire? _____

_____

_____

16. What three cities do Muslims consider sacred? _____

17. What intellectual contributions did Muslims of this period make? _____

_____

_____

Study Guide

Complete the chart to compare Islamic and biblical teaching. Use the box on page 225 of the Student Text and the Bible verses given below.

18.

Difference	Islamic Teaching	Biblical Teaching
View of God (John 10:30; 15:26)		
View of Jesus (Matthew 17:5, John 1:34)		
Mediator between God and people (1 Timothy 2:5)		
Eternity (1 John 5:13)		

First, plan the essay on your own paper. Then, write it below.

19. Compare and contrast the beliefs of Islam with biblical truth. _____

_____

_____

_____

_____

_____

_____

_____

_____

_____

The Byzantine Empire

Complete the organizer as you read about the empire in turmoil and a power struggle in the church.

Empire in Turmoil (p. 227)	
Many wars resulted in . . .	more _____ given to peasants and a rise in _____ .
Civil war weakened the empire for . . .	_____ years.
Leo III had an advantage in fighting his enemies because . . .	he had lived among the _____ and he had lived on the _____ Peninsula.
The Muslims closed off Constantinople by sea, hoping to . . .	_____ the citizens into surrendering.
Leo fought off the Muslim invasion with a new weapon called . . .	_____ _____ , an explosive mixture that would burn on top of water.
Two other factors that allowed the Byzantine Empire to have victory were . . .	a harsh _____ and a _____ that killed many people the next summer.
Power Struggle in the Church (p. 228)	
The most important church leaders were . . .	the _____ in the West and the _____ of Constantinople in the East.
In 1054, the pope tried to take authority over churches . . .	that had been under the _____ authority.
When the patriarch refused the pope's demand, the pope . . .	_____ him. The patriarch then _____ the pope.
The church separated into . . .	the Roman _____ Church in the West and the Eastern _____ Church in the East.
Sacred images of Christ, Mary, the saints, and other sacred subjects are . . .	called _____ .
Leo III thought that icons were . . .	a type of _____ , and he ordered their destruction.

The Byzantine Empire

_____

Complete the organizer as you read about the height of the Byzantine Empire, the Crusades, and the fall of the Byzantine Empire.

Height of the Byzantine Empire (pages 229–30)	
During the height of the Byzantine Empire, the emperors successfully fought . . .	their enemies on the _____ Peninsula and in the _____ _____.
Christian missionaries from Constantinople traveled . . .	throughout eastern _____.
Basil II was a successful emperor and became known as . . .	the _____ _____ because he defeated the Bulgarian army.
After Basil's death, Constantinople lost trade to . . .	_____ and faced attacks from new enemies.
The Seljuk Turks captured . . .	_____ from the Fatimid Caliphate in 1073.

The Crusades (pages 230–31)	
The pope wanted to free Jerusalem, so he started . . .	religious campaigns called the _____.
In the First Crusade, the crusaders were . . .	able to capture _____.
The Second and Third Crusades ended with . . .	the Muslims regaining _____.
The Fourth Crusade ended with the crusaders plundering . . .	the city of _____.

The Recovery of the Byzantine Empire (page 231)	
Some Byzantines fled . . .	to _____ _____ and organized a new empire with the capital at _____.
The emperors worked hard to strengthen the empire, and by the time of Michael VIII, . . .	the army was strong enough to recapture _____.

The Fall of the Byzantine Empire (pages 232–33)	
By 1371, another group of Turks, the Ottomans, had conquered . . .	all of the Byzantine Empire except the city of _____.
Different emperors tried to get help . . .	from _____.
In the 1300s, all Europe was weakened from . . .	a disease called the _____ Death.
By March of 1453, the Ottomans conquered Constantinople by . . .	using _____ to fire on the walls.

Study Guide

Write _True_ if the statement is true. If the statement is false, write the correction for the underlined words.

_____ 1. The purpose of the Crusades was to free Jerusalem from <u>barbarian</u> rule.

_____ 2. The <u>Second</u> Crusade was successful in capturing Jerusalem.

_____ 3. During the <u>Fourth</u> Crusade the crusaders made their own alliances.

_____ 4. The crusaders made a plan to invade other cities because they were short on <u>time</u>.

_____ 5. During the Fourth Crusade, the crusaders and Venetians plundered the city of <u>Carthage</u>.

Complete the statements.

6. Leo III had experience that benefited his rule because _____

_____.

7. Because of his harsh treatment of the Bulgarian captives, Basil II was often called the

_____ _____.

8. Of the new enemies after 1025, the Byzantines especially feared the _____

_____.

9. Because of the Crusades, nobles spent large amounts of _____ and

_____ grew with increased trade.

10. Emperor John III promoted political and _____ reform, helped the

_____, built _____, improved _____ methods, and

built a system of frontier _____.

11. Emperor Michael VIII recaptured the important city of _____.

Answer the questions.

12. What were the three main factors that helped Leo III defeat the Muslim attack on Constantinople?

_____

13. What area of land did Leo III take back from Muslim rule? _____

_____

14. What caused the split between the Eastern and Western branches of the church? _____

_____

15. What are sacred images called that represent Christ, Mary, the saints, or other sacred objects? _____

_____

Study Guide

Write two supporting details for each statement.

16. Leo III considered icons a type of idol.

   _____

   _____

17. The best and most powerful years of the Byzantine Empire were between 850 and 1050.

   _____

   _____

18. Christian missionaries from Constantinople made important contributions in the 860s.

   _____

   _____

First, plan the essay on a sheet of paper. Then, write it below.

19. Compare and contrast the beliefs of the Eastern Orthodox Church with those of Protestants.

   _____

   _____

   _____

   _____

   _____

   _____

   _____

   _____

   _____

   _____

   _____

   _____

   _____

   _____

   _____

   _____

Study Guide

_____

Write _True_ if the statement is true. If the statement is false, write the correction for the underlined words.

_____ 1. The ruler of the Ottomans was called the <u>sultan</u>.

_____ 2. The Turks who conquered all the Byzantine Empire were the <u>Ottomans</u>.

_____ 3. The year the Byzantine Empire fell was <u>1187</u>.

_____ 4. A terrible disease spread by <u>mosquitoes</u> was known as the Black Death.

Complete the statement.

5. The lasting contributions of the Byzantine Empire were that the Roman _____ was kept from disappearing and that scholars preserved Greek learning, philosophy, and _____ and much of what is known about the _____ world.

Identify the numbered places on the map.

6. _____

7. _____

8. _____

9. _____ _(city)_

10. _____ _(water)_

11. _____

12. _____

13. _____

14. _____

15. _____

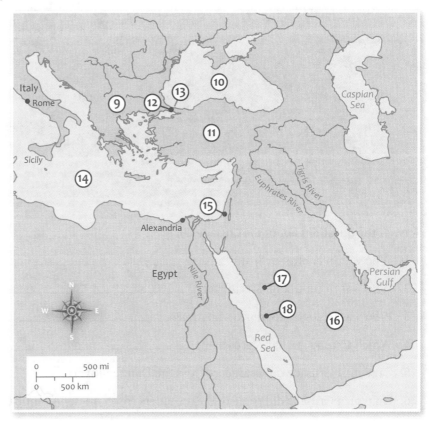

The Crusades

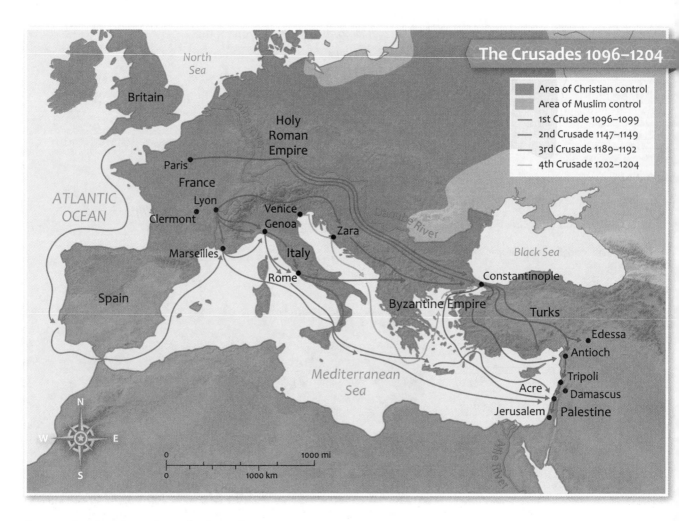

The Crusades 1096–1204

Area of Christian control
Area of Muslim control
— 1st Crusade 1096–1099
— 2nd Crusade 1147–1149
— 3rd Crusade 1189–1192
— 4th Crusade 1202–1204

Answer the questions about the Crusades.

1. Who was in control of Spain? _____

2. Who was in control of Great Britain? _____

3. Who was in control of northern Africa? _____

4. Which Crusade went to Jerusalem? _____

5. On which Crusade did crusaders cross the Danube River? _____

6. On which Crusade did some of the crusaders travel on the Atlantic Ocean? _____

7. Which Crusades left from the city of Lyon? _____

8. Which city did all the Crusades travel to? _____

9. Which Crusades went across Asia Minor? _____

Spread of the Black Death

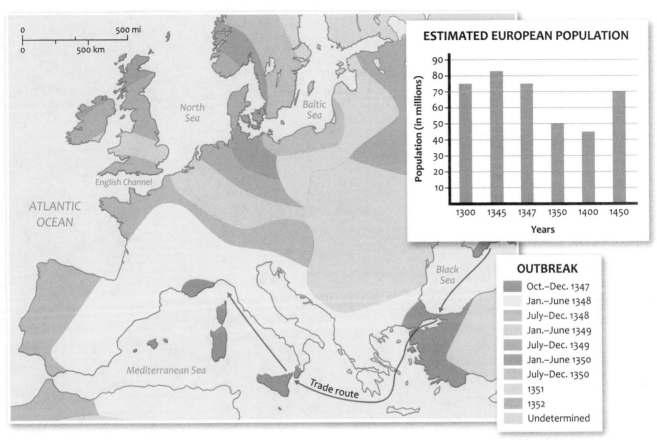

ESTIMATED EUROPEAN POPULATION

OUTBREAK
- Oct.–Dec. 1347
- Jan.–June 1348
- July–Dec. 1348
- Jan.–June 1349
- July–Dec. 1349
- Jan.–June 1350
- July–Dec. 1350
- 1351
- 1352
- Undetermined

Complete the section.

1. By what month and year had the Black Death arrived on the Italian Peninsula? _____

2. By what year had the Black Death reached areas on the Baltic Sea? _____

3. What was the timespan (month and year) over which the Black Death spread through the British Isles?

_____

How many years was that? _____

4. Did the Black Death reach Spain or Sicily first? _____

5. In what year after the Black Death was the population of Europe 70 million? _____

6. What was the difference in population between 1300 and 1450? _____

7. Which year had the greater population, 1300 or 1450? _____

Why? _____

8. In which year shown was Europe's population the smallest? _____

9. By 1450, was the population of Europe back to what it had been before the Black Death? _____

10. What was the timespan (month and year) over which the Black Death spread through Spain?

_____

How many years was this? _____

Mesoamerica

Refer to pages 238–39 to complete the chart with your teacher.

Features of a Civilization	Olmecs
Organized cities and government	
Social classes	
Job specialization	
Arts, sciences, and written language	
Religion	

A jadeite celt engraved with the image of an Olmec deity. What was this celt used for rather than being used as a tool?

Drawing Conclusions

Refer to the topics below to examine the objects in the bag. Record observations below.

buildings
dress
languages
material

numbers
people
religion
words

Items		Observations
1.		
2.		
3.		
4.		
5.		
6.		
7.		
8.		
9.		
10.		

Answer the questions.

11. Do the items in the bag belong to a male or to a female? What items suggest this? _____

_____

12. Are there items that suggest the age of the person? If so, why? _____

_____

13. What items indicate the hobbies or interests the person has? _____

_____

14. Would this person be interested in learning or reading? Are there clues to the answer to this question?

_____

15. Are there clues to this person's heritage or nationality? If so, what? _____

_____

16. What language does the person speak? What items reveal the person's language? _____

_____

Write the identity of the owner.

17. _____

Study Guide

_____

Complete the section.

1. How were ancient American civilizations hidden from the rest of the world? _____

_____

2. Label North America, South America, the Pacific Ocean, and the Gulf of Mexico. Draw the possible migration route early people took.

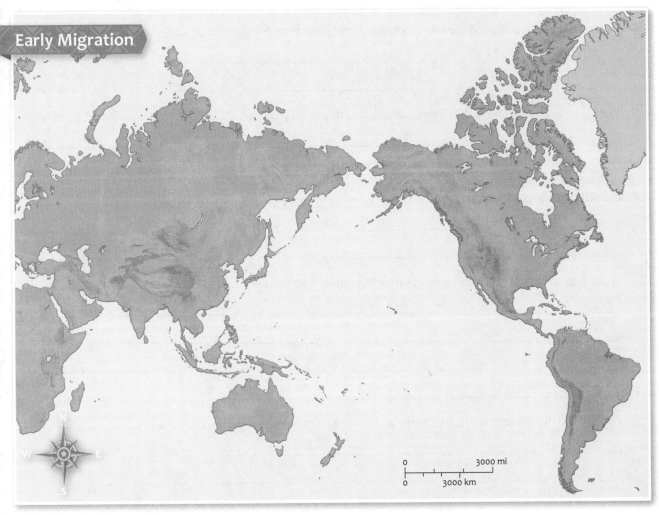

Early Migration

3. Describe geographic features in Mesoamerica and the impact of geography on the development of

civilization. _____

_____

_____

4. What was the geography of the area where the Olmecs first settled? What modern-day country includes the

area the Olmecs settled in? _____

_____

_____

Study Guide

_____

Complete the section.

5. Did the Olmecs use technology in the urban center of San Lorenzo Tenochtitlán? What technology did they use? _____

_____

_____

6. What natural materials did the Olmecs use to build their houses? _____

_____

_____

7. Why is little known about the Olmec culture and their everyday life? _____

_____

_____

8. Describe the large stone carvings the Olmecs are known for. _____

_____

_____

9. What impact did the Olmecs have on other Mesoamerican cultures? _____

_____

_____

_____

_____

10. Explain the importance of the discovery and the use of rubber by the Mesoamericans. _____

_____

_____

_____

_____

Mesoamerica

Complete the chart with your teacher.

Features of a Civilization	Mayas
Organized cities and government	
Social classes	1. 2. 3. 4. This ceramic box, decorated with divine beings, was large enough to hold a Mayan king's clothing or valued books. A ceramic lid would have sealed the box, protecting its contents from water or insect damage.
Job specialization	

Mesoamerica

Features of a Civilization	Mayas
Arts, sciences, and written language	

A Mayan bird-shaped double whistle. The whistle's pitch could be changed by partially covering the hole in the bird's belly while blowing into the tail. A mouthpiece behind the bird's ears created another pitch in a second chamber.

Mesoamerica

Complete the chart with your teacher.

Features of a Civilization	Mayas
Religion	

Rectangular stone altar engraved with portraits of the first sixteen Mayan rulers of Copan, Honduras

Study Guide

_____

Complete the section.

1. What did Diego de Landa do that contributed to the understanding of the Mayan culture? What is the importance of his contributions? _____

   _____

   _____

2. Were Diego de Landa's methods for converting Mayas to Roman Catholicism just or unjust? Why?

   _____

   _____

3. What is the importance of being able to read Mayan hieroglyphics? _____

   _____

   _____

Write the name of the Mayan social class for each description.

_____ 4. top of society, descended from the gods and should be obeyed

_____ 5. bottom of society, included debtors, criminals, and war prisoners

_____ 6. just below kings

_____

_____ 7. did the hard manual work

Mark all the correct answers.

8. The roles of Mayan women included ___.
   - ○ grinding grain and making thread
   - ○ weaving cloth, making clothes, and caring for the children
   - ○ working in the fields while the men and boys prepared the meal

9. Mayan trade included ___.
   - ○ cities in the highlands trading with those in the lowlands
   - ○ trading centers in Spain
   - ○ a means for people to get what they needed

Study Guide

_____

Write _True_ if the statement is true. If the statement is false, write the correction for the underlined words.

_____ 1. Mayas were <u>animists</u> who believed everything had a spiritual esssence.

_____ 2. Each person had a spiritual guide called a <u>priest</u>.

_____ 3. The main clergy of the Yucatec Maya were the <u>Ah Kin</u>.

_____ 4. The Mayas believed the <u>sky</u> was flat and four gods held up each corner.

_____ 5. <u>Heaven</u> had thirteen layers, each with its own god.

_____ 6. The underworld had nine layers, each with a <u>lord</u> of the night.

_____ 7. At death, Mayas worked their way through the layers until they reached the <u>lowest</u> heaven.

_____ 8. People went to the underworld through a <u>cenote</u>.

_____ 9. Kings followed the path of the <u>moon</u> when they died and eventually fell to the underworld.

_____ 10. Those who died from being sacrificed and women who died in childbirth went straight to the supreme <u>underworld</u>.

_____ 11. Almost everyone was buried with a piece of <u>obsidian</u> in his mouth when he died.

_____ 12. Nobles played a ritual ball game which some scholars believe ended in members of the losing team being <u>sacrificed</u> to the gods.

Mark all the correct answers.

13. Posible reasons for the decline of the Mayan civilization would include that ____.

   ○ famine caused people to move away
   ○ war ended the civilization
   ○ the people rebelled against the Mayan way of life

Mesoamerica

Complete the chart with your teacher.

Features of a Civilization	Aztecs
Organized cities and government	
Social classes	
Job specialization	
Arts, sciences, and written language	

Mesoamerica

Complete the chart with your teacher.

Features of a Civilization	Aztecs
Religion	

Female water deity wearing a headdress and the attire of a noblewoman; wife of the rain god, Tlaloc

Study Guide

_____

Write the letter by the corresponding name of each location on the map.

_____ 1. Tenochtitlán

_____ 2. Gulf of Mexico

_____ 3. Pacific Ocean

_____ 4. Valley of Mexico

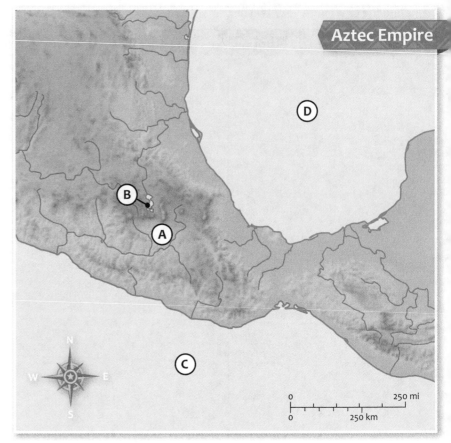

Aztec Empire

Complete the section.

5. What geological features influenced the development of the Aztec civilization? _____

_____

_____

6. What part did religion play in the Aztec culture? _____

_____

_____

_____

_____

_____

Study Guide

Complete the section.

7. What were some consequences of the Spanish invasion of the Aztec civilization? _____

    _____

    _____

    _____

    _____

8. In whose image were the Aztecs and all people made? _____

    _____

Complete the chart to compare the Mayas and the Aztecs.

Mayas	Aztecs
society included kings, priests and nobles, peasant workers	
each city-state had a king	
used hieroglyphics to create books of their writings	
treated unjustly by the Spanish priest Diego de Landa	
made advances in math and astronomy	
practiced trade	
religious beliefs included animism, spiritual guides, rituals based on a calendar; had a supreme deity, priests, ritual bloodletting, and human sacrifice	

Ancient Africa

_____

Complete the outline as you read about the continent of Africa.

I. Africa's Regions: _____, _____, _____,

   _____, and _____

II. Africa's Geography

   A. Location

      1. Africa is surrounded by _____ bodies of water.

      2. The _____ runs through the middle of Africa.

   B. Deserts

      1. The _____, the largest desert in Africa, is in the north.

      2. The Kalahari and the _____ Desert are in the south.

      3. The Sahara has sand, rocky _____, and stony plateaus.

      4. Somalia has a _____ _____ desert.

   C. Lakes and Rivers

      1. Lake _____ is generally considered the source of the White Nile River.

      2. Lake _____ and Lake _____ are man-made lakes.

   D. Tropics

      1. Rainfall can be one hundred inches per year in the _____.

      2. Rainforests have huge _____ and vines and much _____.

      3. The soil in rainforests is not _____, so farming is difficult.

   E. Savanna

      1. The savanna has tall _____ and few _____.

      2. People raise _____ and _____ on the savanna.

   F. Mountains

      1. Mount Kilimanjaro is over _____ thousand feet high.

      2. Some mountains in Africa were formed by _____ activity.

Africa's Regions

Using the glossary in the Student Text or a dictionary, write a definition or description for each word.

1. desert _____

2. equator _____

3. Horn of Africa _____

4. oasis _____

5. rain shadow desert _____

_____

6. rainforest _____

_____

7. sand dune _____

8. savanna _____

Write the five regions of Africa in the key. Color each region and the corresponding rectangle in the key.

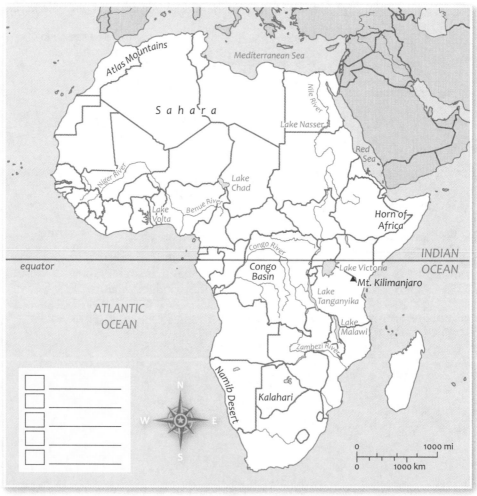

Types of Communities

Examine the geographic features on the map of Africa's regions (page 186) and the natural resources on the map below. Using these sources and information from your textbook, predict the types of occupations that communities might be engaged in for each region of Africa and explain why.

1. Northern _____

_____

_____

2. Western _____

_____

_____

3. Central _____

_____

_____

4. Eastern _____

_____

_____

5. Southern _____

_____

_____

_____

_____

_____

_____

_____

Resources of Africa

🌾 Agriculture	🐄 Livestock
🪨 Coal	🔥 Natural gas
🦴 Copper	⛽ Oil
💎 Diamonds	🧂 Salt
🐟 Fish	🥈 Silver
🟫 Gold	🧊 Sugar
🐪 Herding	⛵ Trade
🪨 Iron ore	☢ Uranium

Ancient Africa

_____

Complete the outline as you read about keys to Africa's past.

I. Africa's Past

  A. Challenges of African history

    1. The ancient Egyptians left _____ records on stone and _____.

    2. Most of the people of ancient Africa did not have a _____ language.

  B. Linguistics

    1. Linguists study _____ and _____ to learn of people's migration routes.

    2. Linguists helped trace the migration route of the _____.

  C. Botany

    1. Botanists can trace the movements of people by their _____.

    2. Botanists can make assumptions about _____ people moved and how their methods of food _____ and production changed.

  D. Archaeology

    1. Discoveries of ancient ruins show _____ people lived and sometimes reveal their _____ of life.

    2. Cave paintings have shown the _____ that early Africans used for fighting and hunting, the types of animals which were hunted, and _____ that may have been part of a written language.

  E. Oral History

    1. Oral history spreads the traditions of a culture from one generation to the next by the _____ word.

    2. Many African villages had _____, who learned their villages' history and passed it on by word of _____.

    3. Modern historians try to evaluate the _____ of a story by comparing it with stories from different _____.

Study Guide

Match the description to the correct term.

_____ 1. an African oral storyteller

_____ 2. an area with tall grasses and few trees

_____ 3. a scientist who studies plants

_____ 4. stories about the past that are spoken instead of written down

_____ 5. a fertile area in the desert with water

_____ 6. a tropical forest filled with huge trees and vines and a large variety of wildlife; receives annual rains of one hundred inches or more

_____ 7. a lowland area that receives little rain; formed when wind blows water vapor high into nearby mountains

_____ 8. a scholar who studies languages

Zebras and blue wildebeest migrate long distances every year to find the grasses that are produced by annual rains.

A botanist	E oral history
B griot	F rain shadow desert
C linguist	G rainforest
D oasis	H savanna

Complete the section.

9. Identify one way that geographers organize Africa for studying. _____

10. Identify the peninsula on the eastern coast of Africa. _____

11. Explain why rain shadow deserts form. _____

_____

_____

12. Name four ways of learning about people and their history other than written records. _____

_____

_____

13. Explain how a historian evaluates the truth of a story that has been passed down orally. _____

_____

_____

14. Identify three land features of Africa. _____

_____

15. Identify the people whose migration route from the Benue River to southern Africa was traced by linguists.

_____

Learning About the Past

Read the following descriptions of historical conclusions (from various parts of the world). Determine the source of historical knowledge that each demonstrates: linguistics, botany, or archaeology.

_____ 1. Coins (or other currency) help the people of a country or empire buy and sell goods. Coins are easy to carry, and they can help determine definite values for goods. Historians have concluded that economic activity was important to the people of Aksum because of the discovery of coins minted by the Aksumite government.

_____ 2. Historians see evidence of African influence in the southeastern United States, starting especially with the time of the international slave trade. Foods like okra that were grown in Western Africa became important parts of the diet of the American South.

_____ 3. Because the common language of eastern Africa's coastal cities, Swahili, contains many Arabic words, historians know that Arabs played an important role in coastal trade.

_____ 4. Based on items like jewelry, pottery, and statues, historians conclude that the Sao of West Africa were skilled in metalworking and advanced in the arts.

_____ 5. Words and constructions of the French language reveal that both the Romans and the Franks, a Germanic tribe, had a historical presence in France.

_____ 6. Maize (corn) appears to have originated in Mesoamerica. Historians can trace the movements of people across the Americas through evidence of maize cultivation.

Corn is an important part of Mexico's cultural heritage and of many Mexicans' daily diet.

Ancient Africa

_____

Complete the outline as you read about Africa's empires.

I. Africa's Empires

  A. Aksum

    1. Aksum traded with _____ and Europeans.

    2. _____ made Christianity the official religion.

    3. Trade dwindled after _____ fell and Muslim armies conquered

    _____.

  B. Ghana

    1. Ghana was located along the _____ River.

    2. _____ was often traded for _____.

    3. In _____ trade, the traders never saw one another.

    4. Ghana's king charged _____ on all trade.

    5. Arabian merchants brought the religion of _____.

  C. Mali

    1. _____ Keita conquered Ghana and took control of trade.

    2. Musa I was known for his _____ and devotion to _____.

    3. On a pilgrimage to _____, Musa gave away much _____.

    4. After Musa's death, there was fighting _____ the empire and attacks from

    _____.

  D. Songhai

    1. Songhai was an important trading town in the _____ Empire.

    2. Under _____ _____, Songhai won independence and conquered

    neighboring cities.

    3. The ruler built _____ to patrol the Niger River and _____ cities

    to rule the empire.

    4. Morocco defeated Songhai with _____ and better-trained _____.

Features of Aksum Civilization

Refer to pages 262–63 to complete the chart with your teacher.

Features of a Civilization	Aksum
Organized cities and government	
Social classes	
Job specialization	
Arts, sciences, and written language	
Religion	

Features of Mali Civilization

_____

Use the information on pages 265–66 to predict what the features of civilization would have been for the Mali Empire.

Features of a Civilization	Mali
Organized cities and government	
Social classes	
Job specialization	
Arts, sciences, and written language	
Religion	

Study Guide

Complete the section.

1. Explain how Christianity became Aksum's official religion. _____

   _____

   _____

2. How did its location and resources help make Ghana a wealthy empire? _____

   _____

   _____

3. Describe how Ghana acquired Islam but kept its traditional beliefs. _____

   _____

   _____

4. Explain how Mali became an empire. _____

   _____

5. Explain how the city of Songhai became an empire. _____

   _____

6. Describe the accomplishments of Sunni Ali as leader of the Songhai Empire. _____

   _____

Write a sentence that tells how the items in each of the following pairs are different from each other.

Example:

    goods traded in Ghana from the south • goods traded in Ghana from the north <u>Gold came up from the south to be traded in Ghana, but salt came down from the north.</u>

7. Aksum's spoken language • Aksum's written language _____

   _____

8. Aksum's location • Ghana's location _____

   _____

9. goods Aksum traded • goods Ghana traded _____

   _____

10. legends about Sundiata Keita • legends about Sunni Ali _____

   _____

   _____

   _____

Study Guide

_____

Write _True_ if the statement is true. If the statement is false, write the correction for the underlined words.

_____ 11. The king of Ghana charged taxes on all <u>trade</u> with his kingdom, making himself wealthy.

_____ 12. The empire of Aksum was ruled by King <u>Frumentius</u>.

_____ 13. Many scholars believe that the kingdom of Sheba was located in what is now <u>Egypt</u>.

_____ 14. Jesus used <u>the queen of Sheba</u> as an example of the eager faith which the Jews should have welcomed Him with.

_____ 15. _Mansa_ was the word for _ruler_ in the <u>Ghanian</u> language.

_____ 16. Ibn Battuta described the people of Mali as <u>just and honest</u>.

_____ 17. <u>Mansa Musa</u> was the strong ruler of Mali who was known as the Lion King.

_____ 18. The city of <u>Koumbi Saleh</u> became Songhai's center of Islamic faith and learning.

Salt and gold (above) were main items of trade in Ghana, while emeralds and myrrh (below) were among Aksum's goods.

Draw a circle around the part of the sentence that states the cause. Underline the part of the sentence that states the effect.

19. Most of the empires in ancient Africa rose to power because of wealth they gained through trade.

20. Because Arabian merchants were Muslims, they introduced the religion of Islam to the people of West Africa.

21. Sundiata Keita built his capital on the main trade route across the Sahara because he had gained control of the gold and salt trade.

22. Mansa Musa was a devout Muslim, so he made a pilgrimage to Mecca.

23. Mansa Musa could take hundreds of pounds of gold to Mecca because he was immensely wealthy.

24. When people received free gold from Mansa Musa, the price of gold dropped.

25. Because there were no more strong kings after Mansa Musa's death, the Malian Empire slowly weakened and broke apart.

26. The Moroccan army was better trained and had muskets; therefore, they defeated the empire of Songhai.

Study Guide

_____

Write *True* if the statement is true. If the statement is false, write the correction for the underlined words.

_____27. The San and the Khoikhoi spoke languages that used <u>clicks</u> for many of their consonants.

_____28. Both the Dutch and the British came to the <u>northern</u> tip of Africa.

_____29. A <u>clan</u> is a group of families descended from a common ancestor.

_____30. The Shona built large <u>mud</u> houses called zimbabwes.

_____31. Historians divide Africa's early peoples into groups according to their <u>occupation</u>.

_____32. <u>Great Zimbabwe</u> was a large zimbabwe that may have been a king's palace.

_____33. Pygmy tribes lived <u>on the savanna</u>.

_____34. As the Bantu moved east and south, some eventually pushed <u>San</u> and Khoikhoi peoples out of their homes.

Complete the charts.

35–37. Describe the dress, the occupations, and the valuable possession of the Tuareg.

Tuareg	
Dress	
Occupations	
Valuable possession	

38–41. List the similarities of the independent cities of eastern Africa's coast.

Coastal Cities	
Religion	
Goods for trade	
Language	
Occupations	

Ancient Africa

_____

Complete the outline as you read about Africa's people and the outside world.

I. Africa's People

   A. Historians divide Africa's peoples by _____.

   B. Northern Africa

      1. Most nomads spoke _____ languages.

      2. The Tuareg were farmers, _____, and traders.

   C. Central Africa

      1. The _____ were skilled in metalworking and advanced

        in the _____.

      2. Pygmy tribes live off the land deep in the _____.

   D. Southern Africa

      1. Some Bantu migrated to the _____ tip of Africa.

      2. The San and Khoikhoi spoke _____ languages.

      3. The Shona built stone houses called _____.

      4. The _____ and British settled in southern Africa.

   E. Eastern Africa

      1. _____ and Persian merchants controlled trading cities.

      2. Coastal cities were predominantly _____ and spoke _____.

II. Africa and the Outside World

   A. The Slave Trade

      1. Civilization and _____ were hindered because of the slave trade.

      2. Slavery was unjust because humans are created in God's _____.

   B. Religion

      1. Christianity spread in _____ and southern Africa.

      2. Though some missionaries mistreated Africans, many _____ them.

Comparing Religions

Masks are frequently used in traditional African religious and social events.

Use the Student Text and the Bible to complete the chart.

Traditional African Beliefs	Christianity
Most Africans believed in a god who was a _____ being, but they relied on _____ to explain what this god was like.	The Bible teaches that God _____ the world (Genesis 1:1). Christians rely on the _____ to explain what God is like (1 Thessalonians 2:13).
Africans believed that their god could be reached through _____ and offerings.	The Bible teaches that only Christ's sacrifice is sufficient to _____ people to God (2 Corinthians 5:19).
One common belief was that there were spirits who controlled natural forces for _____ or for _____. Africans _____ these spirits and tried to please them.	The Bible teaches that there is only _____ God (Isaiah 45:5). He created all things for His own _____; only He is _____ to receive glory (Revelation 4:11).
Africans often relied on a person thought to have magical powers, such as a _____ man or a _____, to connect them with the supernatural world.	The Bible teaches that Jesus is the _____ between God and man whose death provided atonement for man's sin (1 Timothy 2:5). He makes _____ for people who come to God by Him (Hebrews 7:25).
Africans believed that the spirits of their departed relatives _____ them and _____ their lives.	The Bible warns people not to try to _____ the dead (Deuteronomy 18:10–11; a necromancer is a person who inquires of the dead).

Study Guide

Complete the section.

1. Why did the international trade of African slaves become widespread in the 1600s? _____

   _____

   _____

   _____

2. Describe the cultural and moral effects of the slave trade on Africa. _____

   _____

   _____

   _____

3. Evaluate the influence of Christian missions on Africa. _____

   _____

   _____

   _____

Plan the essay on a sheet of paper, then write it below.

4. Contrast traditional African beliefs with biblical truth.

   _____

   _____

   _____

   _____

   _____

   _____

   _____

   _____

   _____

   _____

Study Guide

_____

Write the number of each place on the map.

5. Atlantic Ocean
6. Horn of Africa
7. Indian Ocean
8. Kalahari
9. Madagascar
10. Nile River
11. Sahara
12. Timbuktu

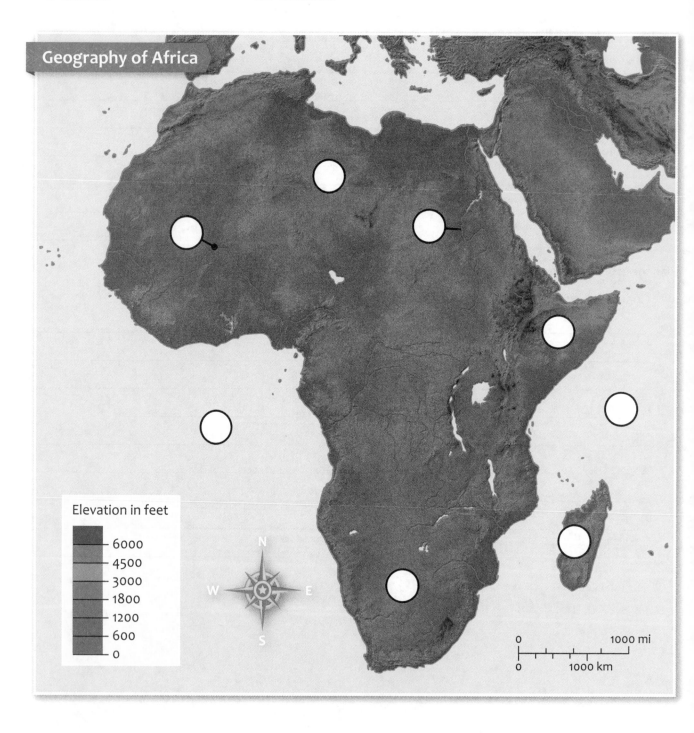

Geography of Africa

Elevation in feet

- 6000
- 4500
- 3000
- 1800
- 1200
- 600
- 0

N
W E
S

0   1000 mi
0   1000 km

Ancient Japan

Refer to the Student Text to complete each statement.

1. The four main islands of Japan are _____, _____, _____, and _____. (page 278)

2. Japan is an _____, which is a large group of islands. (page 278)

3. A creation myth says Japan formed from _____ of water that fell from the _____ of a god and a goddess. (page 278)

4. Bodies of water surrounding Japan include the East China Sea, the _____ of _____, and the _____ _____. (page 279)

5. The highest mountain in Japan is _____ _____. (page 279)

6. The _____ were named by archaeologists who found pottery made in a _____ pattern. (page 280)

7. _____ came to Japan and mingled with the Jomon. (page 280)

8. Historians believe the _____ are the main ancestors of the _____ people. (page 280)

9. These ancestors _____ pottery and painted it _____. (page 280)

10. Japanese people divided into _____, each with its own warrior _____. (page 280)

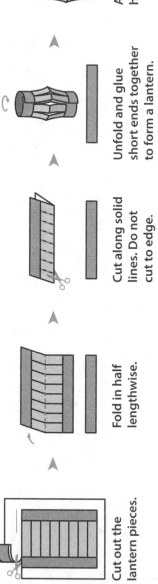

Cut out the
lantern pieces.

Fold in half
lengthwise.

Cut along solid
lines. Do not
cut to edge.

Unfold and glue
short ends together
to form a lantern.

Attach
handle.

Ancient Japan

Refer to the Student Text to complete each statement.

1. The _____ clan rose to power and formed strong _____ states. (page 281)

2. This clan was influenced by the _____ and the Koreans. (page 281)

3. The Yamato period was also known as the _____ period. (page 281)

4. The ruling family claimed a relationship with _____ _____. (page 281)

5. Prince _____ developed a _____ that became the basis of the imperial government. (page 281)

6. The prince spread the religion of _____ in Japan. (page 282)

7. In _____, the kami and the _____ are worshiped. (page 282)

8. The Japanese learned to write _____ from Chinese Buddhist _____. (page 283)

9. A time of _____ and _____ changes came during the Great Change or the _____ _____. (page 283)

10. The leaders of Japan weakened the influence of clan _____ by modeling their government after _____ government. (page 283)

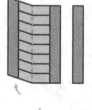

Attach
handle.

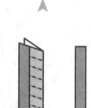

Unfold and glue
short ends together
to form a lantern.

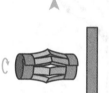

Cut along solid
lines. Do not
cut to edge.

Fold in half
lengthwise.

Cut out the
lantern pieces.

Study Guide

Write the name of the place that corresponds to the number on the map.

1. _____

2. _____

3. _____

4. _____

5. _____

6. _____

7. _____

8. _____

9. _____

10. _____

11. _____

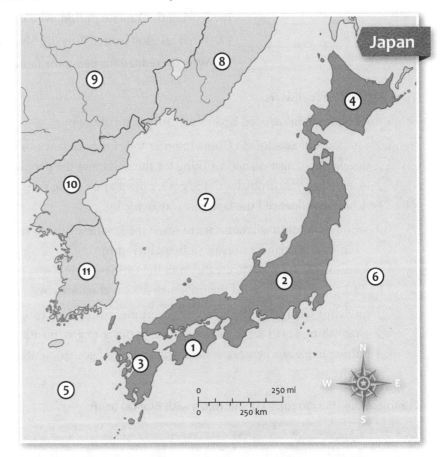

Complete the section.

12. How does Japan form an archipelago? _____

_____

_____

13. Why is little known about Japan's early history? _____

_____

_____

14. What civilizations influenced Japan? _____

_____

_____

15. How did the Yamato come to power in Japan? _____

_____

_____

Study Guide

_____

Answer the questions.

_____ 16. During the Yamato period, who did each emperor claim was their ancestor?

_____ 17. What religion from China did Shotoku introduce to Japan?

_____ 18. Who is credited for being the father of calligraphy?

Mark all the correct answers.

19. Prince Shotoku influenced Japanese history and culture by ___.

○ sending ambassadors to China in order to bring back its culture, economy, and politics

○ developing irrigation and working for the welfare of the people

○ assembling the chronicles of the government and setting rules for officials in the constitution

20. The Chinese influenced the Japanese way of life by ___.

○ sending Buddhist missionaries to teach the Japanese how to read and write Chinese

○ teaching the Japanese to read Chinese literature

○ teaching the Japanese to create art in the Chinese style

21. The Taika Reform weakened the influence of clan chieftains by ___.

○ modeling changes in the Japanese government after the strong centralized Chinese government

○ establishing a civil service examination in order to give positions to Buddhist priests

○ putting in place a new tax system which allowed governmental officials to gather taxes instead of the chieftains

Complete the chart to contrast Shintoism with Biblical truth.

🏯 Shintoism	✝ Biblical Truth
The main problem with the world is that _____ is out of harmony with _____.	_____ is the main _____ with the world.
If people practice _____ rituals, people can develop a connection with _____, the spirits in _____, to bring about _____ and harmony in this life.	Sin disrupts people's _____ with each other, with _____, and with _____. There is only _____ God. _____ are spirit beings, but they are not tied to features of the _____ world. A truly prosperous life involves being made _____ with God by having sins _____.

Ancient Japan

Refer to the Student Text to complete each statement.

1. The _____ court was a group of nobles who served the _____ in Heian-kyo. (page 284)

2. The court become the center of _____ and _____. (page 284)

3. The official language of the nobles was _____. (page 285)

4. The Japanese wrote their _____ by adapting Chinese characters. (page 285)

5. Writing was popular among nobles, especially _____ who wrote in _____. (page 285)

6. _____ _____ was a great writer who wrote the world's first _____. (page 285)

7. A Japanese form of poetry that is still popular today is the _____. (page 285)

8. Japanese art is characterized by its _____ _____. (page 286)

9. The Japanese art form called *ikebana* arranges _____ to match the occasion and the _____. (page 286)

10. Nobles liked simple, _____ designs for some buildings, which they surrounded with elegant _____ and _____. (page 286)

Cut out the lantern pieces.

Fold in half lengthwise.

Cut along solid lines. Do not cut to edge.

Unfold and glue short ends together to form a lantern.

Attach handle.

Ancient Japan

Refer to the Student Text to complete each statement.

1. During the _____ period, the Japanese blended Shintoism with _____. (page 287)

2. The _____ family sought to _____ the government. (page 287)

3. The Fujiwara married their daughters to sons of the _____ family, and when _____ were born, the Fujiwara ruled as _____. (page 287)

4. A power struggle among clans ended with the _____ creating a government run by _____ _____. (page 287)

5. _____ developed where the ruler divided the _____ among nobles, who then subdivided it among the _____. (page 290)

6. The military leader, called the _____, was chosen by the emperor and given supreme _____ power. (page 290)

7. The _____ were the chief nobles or powerful _____. (page 290)

8. _____ were warriors who mastered _____, fencing, archery, and _____. (page 290)

9. _____ were in the lowest class of the Japanese feudal system and were divided into _____. (page 290)

10. Victory over the _____ drained Japan's _____, which resulted in power _____. (page 291)

Cut out the lantern pieces.

Fold in half lengthwise.

Cut along solid lines. Do not cut to edge.

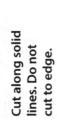

Unfold and glue short ends together to form a lantern.

Attach handle.

Study Guide

Mark all the correct answers.

1. During the Heian period, ____.

   ○ the arts in ancient Japan entered their golden age
   ○ the Japanese developed a spoken language
   ○ the Japanese developed their own artistic patterns

2. After the Japanese blended Shintoism and Buddhism, ____.

   ○ they kept separate the divine beings of Buddhism and Shintoism
   ○ they worshiped in Shinto shrines to obtain help for their daily lives
   ○ they worshiped in Buddhist temples to prepare for the life to come

Plan the essay on a sheet of paper. Then write the essay in the space below.

3. Explain how the Fujiwara family unjustly rose to power.

   _____

   _____

   _____

   _____

   _____

   _____

   _____

   _____

   _____

Write _True_ if the statement is true. If the statement is false, write the correction for the underlined words.

_____ 4. Feudalism developed during the late Heian period.

_____ 5. The ruler divided the treasury among the nobles, then subdivided it among the peasants.

_____ 6. The peasants were to show happiness and allegiance in exchange for land.

_____ 7. Artisans were the highest ranking peasants.

_____ 8. Merchants were the lowest subclass, as they relied on others for their living.

Study Guide

Match each term with the correct description.

_____ 9. the person at the top of the feudal system, along with his family and the military leader

_____ 10. the lowest social class of the feudal system and divided into subclasses

_____ 11. the class just below the top class that included chief nobles or powerful warlords

_____ 12. the second-lowest class that made up the armies

_____ 13. military leader in the top class who was given supreme political authority

A samurai
B peasants
C daimyo
D shogun
E emperor

Complete the section.

14. What caused the Japanese victory during the second invasion by the Mongols? _____

_____

_____

_____

_____

_____

The Middle Ages in Europe

Refer to Student Text page 294 to complete the chart.

Main Idea	Details
The Roman Empire was weakened by _____ tribes conquering its cities.	The great empire had been replaced by small _____ governed by _____ heroes. After the fall of the _____ Empire, Europe entered into a new era called the _____ period. Another term for this period is the _____ _____. This period is the border between the _____ world and the _____ world.
The _____ _____ Church grew more powerful in the _____.	The only source of _____ and authority among Roman citizens was the local _____. Many of the invading _____ rulers had converted to a form of _____, but they followed a form of _____. This belief teaches that God the Son is _____ from and lesser than God the Father. Christians condemned Arianism as _____. After Germanic warriors conquered _____ lands, their rulers _____ the beliefs of the Roman Catholic Church. This was a way that rulers could gain _____ from the local people and from the _____ leaders. The quality of life in most of Europe began to _____. Roads became _____ with weeds, trade _____, and cities stood in _____. People built _____ and worked to _____ _____ for their families. Invaders brought disorder and destruction.

The people of the former Roman Empire needed a place to turn for _____. Without an _____ to guide them, many turned to local _____ and to the Roman _____ Church.

Arian baptistery from the fifth century, Ravenna, Italy

The Middle Ages in Europe

Refer to Student Text page 296 to complete the chart.

The Roman Catholic Church

Church Leadership

1. The pope was the _____ of the Roman Catholic Church. Most _____ followed his leadership.

2. The bishops were _____ the pope. The _____ and the _____ directed the activities of the _____ during the Middle Ages.

3. _____ were clergymen who lived among the people. They led the _____ and instructed people in how to live and _____. They preserved and developed many of the _____ that Christians hold today. However, over time, the priests taught that the church and its leaders played a role in _____. Many of them taught that people needed the help of a priest to receive God's _____. Priests taught that people normally had to receive the _____ to be saved.

4. Monks lived in large _____. These clergymen vowed to never _____ but instead to devote their lives to _____ the Roman Catholic Church. One famous monk was _____. He founded a monastery and wrote a set of _____ for monks to follow. This set of rules was called the _____ _____. Some monks learned to _____ and _____. These monks copied the _____ and writings from the early centuries of the church.

5. _____, like monks, were clergymen who dedicated their lives to service. Neither monks nor friars owned _____. Friars lived among the _____ and were traveling _____.

6. Some women _____ their lives to the church. These women who took religious vows were called _____. They lived in _____.

The Middle Ages in Europe

Refer to Student Text page 297 to complete the chart.

The Roman Catholic Church	
Catholic Beliefs	The Roman Catholic Church teaches that _____ is needed to remove the sin that all people have. Baptism is the means by which a person is initially _____. Righteousness that comes at baptism is maintained through _____ rightly and doing _____ when one sins. The _____ is important for maintaining the _____ begun in baptism. People who would later be called Protestants tried to _____ the Roman Catholic Church to a _____ biblical position. At the heart of the Protestant position was the belief that the teachings regarding _____, _____, and the _____ were not found in the Bible. Protestants argued that the _____ teaches that justification comes through _____ alone. Although Christians need to _____ of their sins and _____ them to God, many Protestants concluded they do not need to confess them to a _____.
The Sacraments	The Roman Catholic Church developed _____ sacraments it believed were necessary for receiving _____ needed for salvation. 1. _____ removes original sin from _____ and original sin and all subsequent sins from _____. 2. _____ gives the Holy Spirit to _____ members of the Roman Catholic Church. 3. The _____ gives grace to members of the church by presenting them with the sacrificed _____ and _____ of Christ in the form of bread and wine. 4. _____ enables people to merit forgiveness for sins committed _____ baptism. 5. _____ _____ are given to a seriously ill or dying person to provide _____ of their sins. 6. _____ _____ give priests the _____ to absolve sin and to conduct the Eucharist. 7. _____ gives grace to a husband and wife in marriage to strengthen their union and make it _____.

Study Guide

_____

Complete the section.

1. What major events began the medieval period? _____

_____

_____

2. What conditions in the Roman Empire increased the influence of the Roman Catholic Church? _____

_____

_____

_____

_____

_____

_____

_____

Refer to the map on Student Text page 295 to answer the question.

3. Which of the medieval kingdoms shown on the map has the most territory? _____

_____

Write the name of the modern-day country or body of water shown on the map.

A. _____

B. _____

C. _____

D. _____

E. _____

F. _____

G. _____

H. _____

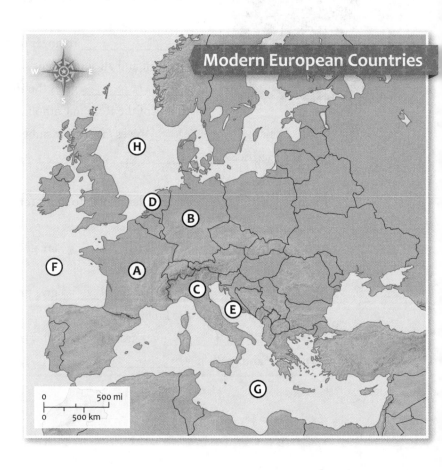

Modern European Countries

Study Guide

Match the position held in the medieval Catholic Church with its description.

_____ 12. served as traveling ministers with the main goal of teaching people to live good lives

_____ 13. led services and instructed people how to live and worship; developed and preserved many Christian doctrines

_____ 14. devoted their lives to the church, took vows, and lived in convents

_____ 15. served as the patriarch of the Roman Catholic Church

_____ 16. served as church leaders within districts, helped the church patriarch direct the activities of the clergy

_____ 17. lived in monasteries; copied the Scriptures and writings from the early centuries of the church

> **A** pope
> **B** bishop
> **C** priest
> **D** monk
> **E** friar
> **F** nun

Complete the chart.

Beliefs of Medieval Roman Catholicism	Biblical Beliefs
_____ is needed to remove sin. Baptism is the means by which a person is _____.	Justification comes through _____ alone.
The righteousness that comes at baptism is maintained through _____ rightly and doing _____ when one sins.	Christ has _____ for the sins of Christians. Christians need to _____ of their sins and _____ them to God.

Answer the question.

18. What role did Benedict play in defining the lifestyle of a monk? _____

_____

_____

_____

_____

_____

_____

The Middle Ages in Europe

Refer to Student Text pages 298–99 to complete the chart.

Topic	Details
Clovis	After Rome fell, the _____ invaded Europe. These people lived in wealthy Roman provinces in _____ and gained the _____ of the Roman Catholic Church. Over the centuries, they formed a _____. The first king was _____, who conquered the last of the Romans in Gaul. The Franks drove out the _____ from southern Gaul. The conquests of Clovis shaped a _____ that would later be called _____.
Charles Martel	During the 700s, Charles Martel became _____ of the Frankish palace and _____ the Franks. Charles was called _____, which means "the _____." The empire ruled by his descendants was called the _____ _____.
Pepin the Short	Charles Martel's son _____ _____ _____ ruled for ten years as mayor of the palace before becoming _____ of the Franks. Before Pepin became king, Pope Stephen II asked him to _____ Rome against the _____. In exchange for his help, the pope publicly _____ Pepin's taking the Frankish crown away from the _____. Pepin _____ the Lombards and gave part of the _____ lands to the church leaders. The church called these lands the _____ _____.
Charlemagne	The greatest Carolingian king was Pepin's son _____. The title *Charlemagne* means _____ _____ _____. Pope Leo III crowned Charlemagne _____, reviving the _____ Roman Empire. Charlemagne extended the _____ kingdom. He divided his lands into small _____, each having several _____. Under Charlemagne's rule, the importance of _____ expanded throughout the _____. Charlemagne invited _____ to his royal court to study and to train others. He started schools for _____ from both noble and _____ families. Charlemagne reformed _____ in his empire. Pendant belonging to Charlemagne

The Middle Ages in Europe

Fifteenth century miniature representing the Treaty of Verdun, which divided the Carolingian Empire between Louis the German, Louis the Pious, and Lothair

Refer to Student Text page 300 to answer the questions.

1. Who inherited the empire after Charlemagne's death? Why did the empire weaken under his rule? _____

_____

_____

2. What led to the division of the empire after the death of Louis the Pious? _____

_____

_____

3. Which of the sons of Louis the Pious ruled over the West Franks? _____

4. Which son ruled the East Franks? _____

5. What people did Lothair rule? _____

6. For what modern-day countries did these areas form a basis? _____

7. How did the languages in the western and eastern parts of the empire change? _____

_____

_____

_____

8. Why was the language inconsistent in the empire? _____

_____

_____

_____

The Middle Ages in Europe

_____

Refer to Student Text page 301 to complete the chart.

Topic	Details
Vikings	The remains of Charlemagne's weakened empire became prey for _____. Many of the invaders were from _____. The Vikings raided different parts of _____. They attacked _____ and then invaded the _____ in Western Europe. The Vikings attacked the modern-day countries of Germany, _____, Spain, and the _____ _____. Eventually, the Vikings began attacking with the intent to _____ and establish new _____. One group of Vikings settled near the _____ _____ in what is today northern _____. One Carolingian king made a treaty with their _____. This settlement gradually developed into the region that became known as _____. Its inhabitants were called _____. In the mid-800s, _____ Vikings began attacking _____. Danish settlers flocked to England to _____ in a large region that became known as the _____. Though they only briefly established _____ control over most of England, the Danes left a mark on English _____.
Norse Mythology	The Norse worshiped many _____. The chief god's name was _____. He was the god of _____, creation, and the _____. He had a wife who was called _____. _____, the god of _____, was under Odin. Thor controlled the wind and rain and was the _____ of the gods. Some modern names of the days of the week come from names of _____ gods. _____ comes from Tiu, the Anglo-Saxon word for the Norse god of war, _____. Wednesday comes from the _____ god, Odin, or the Anglo-Saxon god _____. Thursday is named for _____. Friday is named after _____.

Viking stone relief of Odin receiving warriors of valor in Valhalla, the hall of the slain dead, represented as a palace, Sweden, ca. AD 1000

Study Guide

Match the description with the correct Frankish king.

_____ 1. became mayor of the Frankish palace and united the Franks; his descendants rule the Carolingian Empire

_____ 2. first Frankish king; conquests shaped a nation that would later become the French nation

_____ 3. son of Charles Martel; gave conquered Lombard lands to the leaders of the Roman Catholic Church

_____ 4. greatest of the Frankish kings; crowned by the pope as emperor of the Western Roman Empire

A	Charlemagne
B	Charles Martel
C	Clovis
D	Pepin the Short

Mark all the correct answers.

5. Because of the alliance between Pepin the Short and the Roman Catholic Church, ___.

   ○ the pope officially approved Pepin's taking the Frankish crown away from the Merovingians
   ○ the church leaders received conquered lands after Pepin defeated the Lombards
   ○ there was little conflict between politics and religion for several centuries

6. Charlemagne ___.

   ○ was successful on the battlefield during his military campaigns
   ○ extended the Frankish kingdom to its greatest size
   ○ ended the Western Empire by being crowned emperor

7. The Frankish empire was divided because ___.

   ○ Louis the Pious inherited the empire and was unsuccessful in ruling such a large empire
   ○ Louis's sons worked together to rule a united empire
   ○ each of Louis's sons received a share of the empire, but they had many wars with each other

8. At the time of the division of the Frankish Empire, ___.

   ○ the languages of the Franks in the western and eastern parts of the empire began to change
   ○ western Frankish was developing into French, and eastern Frankish was developing into German
   ○ language throughout the Frankish empire was consistent

Write _True_ if the statement is true. If the statement is false, write the correction for the underlined words.

_____ 9. Scandinavian invaders that raided different parts of Europe were <u>Vikings</u>.

_____ 10. The chief Norse god was <u>Thor</u>.

_____ 11. The <u>Franks</u> were the first European people to discover Iceland, Greenland, and the North American Atlantic coast.

_____ 12. Viking attacks changed in purpose from attacking just to raid to attacking to <u>conquer</u>.

Study Guide

_____

Answer the questions.

13. What caused feudalism to arise during the Middle Ages? _____

_____

14. What did a noble receive for performing a service to the king? _____

_____

15. What did a vassal receive in exchange for his loyal service to the lord? _____

_____

16. Who played an important role in protecting people and property during feudalism? _____

_____

Write _True_ if the statement is true. If the statement is false, write the correction for the underlined words.

_____ 17. Feudalism <u>lacked</u> the unity of a strong central government and military, resulting in conflicts between rival lords and their armies.

_____ 18. Feudal lords had almost <u>no</u> control over the residents of their manors.

_____ 19. Peasants <u>could not</u> appeal legal decisions since the lord's decision was final.

_____ 20. Peasants had <u>little</u> freedom and opportunity.

Plan the essay on a sheet of paper. Write the essay in the space below.

21. Describe the steps in becoming a knight. Include the terms _page_ and _squire_.

_____

_____

_____

_____

_____

_____

_____

_____

_____

_____

_____

_____

_____

_____

_____

The Middle Ages in Europe

Refer to Student Text pages 308–10 to complete the chart.

Topic	Details
The Battle of Hastings	The king of England died in 1066 without an _____. Two nobles, _____ Godwinson and Duke _____ of Normandy, both claimed the _____. Harold set himself up as the next _____. William asked his vassals to provide him with _____ and supplies to form an _____. William and his army met Harold's force on a _____ near the town of _____. _____ forced William to attack _____ by placing his men along the _____ of a hill. Harold's men stood _____ by side with _____ raised, forming a wall of shields. William and the _____ army attacked the _____ again and again. The Norman army finally _____ through. Harold was _____ in the fierce struggle, and his army _____ soon afterward. All England became a _____ kingdom. William was now the _____ of England. He was called William the _____. He began a royal line called the _____.
Henry's Legal System	Norman kings were replaced by the _____ when Henry II came to power in 1154. Henry developed England's _____ system. During Henry's time, courts practiced _____ by _____. The accused person's hands and feet were _____ with rope and the person was thrown into deep _____. The people believed that if he _____, the pure water had _____ him because of his sin, and he was considered _____. If he sank, he was _____. Henry developed procedures to settle _____ claims. He issued _____ to local sheriffs. The writ instructed the sheriff to _____ who actually held each piece of disputed land. The sheriff's decision required a _____ by _____. With the help of the jury, the _____ determined who should be the _____. When there was a _____ over the sheriff's decision, the case could be _____. When there was a _____ case, it would be sent directly to _____ for his decision. Over time, such decisions were written down and _____ throughout England, becoming England's _____ _____.

The Middle Ages in Europe

_____

Refer to Student Text pages 310–11 to complete the chart.

Topic	Details
The Signing of the Magna Carta	In 1199, Henry II's son, _____, became the king of England. King John was not _____ with the people. He imposed heavy _____ on the people to pay for his _____ losses. He used his power to gain _____ and _____ for himself. John was often at odds with the _____. He got into a dispute with the _____ over who should choose the _____ of Canterbury. The pope _____ him for a time. Dissatisfaction with King John's reign _____. A group of _____ examined _____ laws and determined that King John's abuses of power were _____ their rights. The nobles agreed that the king's power needed to be _____.

In 1215, the nobles led a _____ against King John. One of the demands to end the conflict required that _____ sign a document called the _____ _____.

The Magna Carta was based on English _____ from the time of the _____ kings. The _____ designed the document to ensure that their own _____ were protected. English _____ came to view the Magna Carta as a statement of the rights of all _____. Under the Magna Carta, the king had to _____ to the law. The Magna Carta gave the nobles _____ to compel the king to _____.

John _____ the Magna Carta. It was confirmed by the king's _____ and approved by the _____. The document continues to be a _____ of rights for _____ citizens.

Simple Machines

Read the information before completing the activity on the following pages.

People who lived in the Middle Ages used simple machines to make their work easier. These simple machines can be seen in defenses used in castle architecture, medieval weapons, and other machines. In this activity, you will identify the following types of simple machines.

1. The **lever** is any bar that turns on a fixed point, such as a seesaw. It is used to move or raise something.

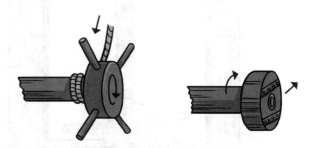

2. A **wheel and axle** is a wheel with a rod running through the wheel. Turning the wheel winds or unwinds a chain or rope on the axle.

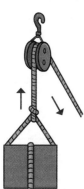

3. A **pulley** has a grooved wheel with a rope or chain that runs in the groove. The rope or chain is pulled through the groove, changing the direction of the pull and making it easier to move a load.

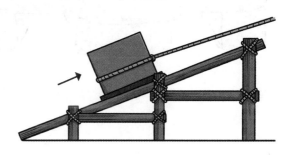

4. An **inclined plane** is a ramp (a flat, sloped surface). A load can be raised or lowered by sliding or rolling it on an inclined plane.

5. A **screw** is an inclined plane wound around an axle.

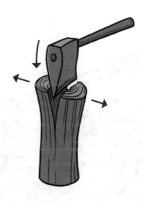

6. A **wedge** is an inclined plane made of wood or metal used to force materials apart. The wedge has a thicker end for the person to hold and a thinner end that can be inserted in a narrow crack to split something apart.

Simple Machines

Olive Press

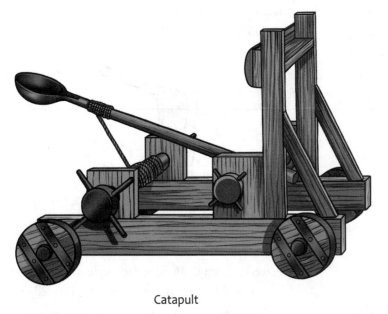

Catapult

1. Circle the screw being used in the olive press. Explain how it is being used.

   _____

   _____

   _____

   _____

   _____

   _____

   _____

   _____

2. Circle the lever used in the catapult. Explain how they are being used.

   _____

   _____

   _____

   _____

   _____

   _____

   _____

   _____

3. Circle the different types of wheels and axles being used in the catapult. Explain how they are being used.

   _____

   _____

   _____

   _____

   _____

   _____

   _____

   _____

Simple Machines

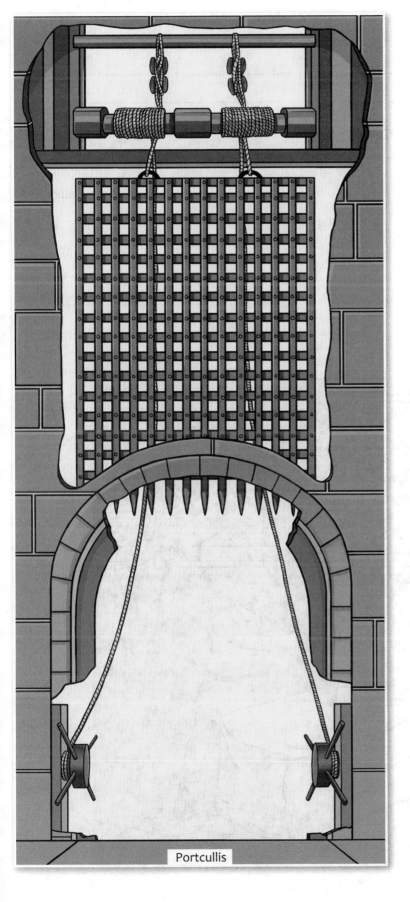

Portcullis

4. Circle the pulleys used in the portcullis. Explain how they are being used.

_____

_____

_____

_____

_____

_____

_____

_____

5. Circle the wheels and axles being used in the portcullis. Explain how they are being used.

_____

_____

_____

_____

_____

_____

_____

_____

Simple Machines

6. Circle the pulley being used in the scene below. Explain how it is being used.

_____

_____

_____

_____

7. Circle the inclined plane being used in the scene below. Explain how it is being used.

_____

_____

_____

_____

8. Circle the wedge being used in the scene below. Explain how it is being used.

_____

_____

_____

_____

Simple Machines

Name an object used today that contains a simple machine.
Explain how that simple machine is used in the object.

9. lever _____

_____

_____

10. wheel and axle _____

_____

_____

11. pulley _____

_____

_____

12. inclined plane _____

_____

_____

13. screw _____

_____

_____

14. wedge _____

_____

_____

The Middle Ages in Europe

_____

Refer to Student Text pages 314–15 to complete the chart.

The Decline of Feudalism	Details
Politics	Trial by _____ gave more authority to royal officials, resulting in less _____ and authority for _____ lords.
Famine and Plague	The famine and the plague weakened Europe's feudal _____. Feudal lords lost much _____ and authority through the _____ declines of this period.
War	A series of wars between England and France became known as the _____ Years' War. These conflicts _____ feudalism in both countries by shifting _____ from feudal lords to _____ and common people.
Conflict between Church and State	One of the conflicts that weakened the feudal system was the _____ over who should appoint _____ officials. Bishops and abbots were being chosen by _____ and _____ and treated as their vassals. As popes worked to _____ the church, they tried to _____ this practice. When Henry IV and Gregory VII fought over who should be the bishop of _____, the pope _____ Henry, and Henry's great lords forced him to seek the pope's _____. Eventually, Henry became stronger and _____ his lords and the pope. The emperor gained some _____ at the expense of the nobles. The compromise _____ that later settled the controversy allowed the church to _____ its own officials.
The Crusades	By the late 1000s, most of the Byzantine Empire had fallen to _____ invaders. The _____ called for Western Europeans to join the Byzantines in a _____ to recapture the Holy Land from the _____. This crusade was the first in a series of _____ wars between the _____ and the Muslim Turks. Western _____ came in contact with other civilizations and _____ during the Crusades. The crusaders brought back goods such as _____, _____, and _____. They returned with the knowledge of how to build better _____, a development that contributed to a coming age of world _____. _____ with other civilizations grew.

The Middle Ages in Europe

Refer to Student Text page 315 to complete the chart.

The Decline of Feudalism	Details
The Great Schism	An argument about who the _____ pope was divided the _____. This disagreement was called the Great _____ Schism. The _____ of Pisa's failed attempt at resolving the problem resulted in the election of _____ popes. The Council of _____ eventually met to find a _____. The _____ elected a pope that the members of the church would _____ of, ending the _____ _____.
A Time of Transition	_____ ran central _____ all over Europe by the year 1500. More people were living in towns and _____ rather than on _____. _____ formed in cities where prominent teachers lived. A revival of _____ began to sweep across Europe and result in new _____ and accomplishments. The modern era of history was about to begin with a _____ revival. Scholars and thinkers were beginning to question the _____ and _____ of the Roman Catholic Church. Their efforts to return to the teachings and practices of _____ would eventually lead to the _____ _____.
The Renaissance	The _____ was a time that began in Italy around AD 1400. The term *renaissance* refers to the rebirth of _____. Programs of study sprang up to prepare people for secular work. These programs looked to the _____ world for examples of things such as how to draw up a _____. Scholars rediscovered works of ancient _____, inspiring a period of great cultural change. These discoveries spread into other parts of _____ over the next _____ hundred years and influenced the culture.

John Wycliffe

Read the information.

Medieval Oxford, a city in England, had close ties to the king and to the political pulse of the whole country. Oxford's university was the center of intellectual activity and influenced the thinking of men across England. It was to Oxford's university that John Wycliffe went, as a youth from Yorkshire in northern England, to be a student. After getting a bachelor's degree in theology, he continued to be interested in biblical studies. Because of interruptions caused by the Black Death, he was not able to earn his doctorate until 1372. By then, he was already considered Oxford's leading philosopher and theologian. In 1374, Wycliffe became a rector, or member of the clergy over a church, in Lutterworth.

The pope demanded that the people of England pay Rome financial support. England was struggling to raise money to resist a possible French attack. Wycliffe advised his local lord to tell Parliament not to send any money. He argued that the church was already too wealthy. Wycliffe said that Christ had called His disciples to poverty and not wealth. He felt that the local authorities should keep the taxes. These opinions got Wycliffe into trouble with the church. The pope issued five bulls, or church edicts, against him. The church in England brought him to trial three times, and two more popes summoned him to Rome. Wycliffe was never put in prison, nor did he ever go to Rome.

Wycliffe wrote about the conflicts with the church. He believed the pope and the church were second in authority to the Word of God. He disagreed with the Roman Catholic Church, who believed that the bread and the wine taken at communion were changed into the body and blood of Christ. Wycliffe believed that "the bread while becoming by virtue of Christ's words the body of Christ does not cease to be bread." From his studying, he disagreed with the church about confessions. "Private confession and the whole system of medieval confession was not ordered by Christ and was not used by the Apostles, for of the three thousand who were turned to Christ's Law on the Day of Pentecost, not one of them was confessed to a priest . . . It is God who is the forgiver."

Wycliffe felt that the common person should read about God's faith in his own language. He said that "Christ and His Apostles taught the people in the language best known to them. It is certain that the truth of the Christian faith becomes more evident the more faith itself is known. Therefore, the doctrine should not only be in Latin but in the vulgar tongue." So Wycliffe and some of his fellow scholars translated the Bible from the Latin Vulgate into English without the church's approval. Although Wycliffe was not alive when the translation was completed, he is credited with the first English translation of the Bible.

Wycliffe died in 1384 after his second stroke. In 1415, the Council of Constance condemned Wycliffe on 260 different counts and ordered that his writings be burned. His bones were dug up and cast out of consecrated ground. In 1428, the pope commanded that his remains be dug up again, burned, and scattered into the River Swift. Wycliffe is considered by many to be the forerunner of the Protestant Reformation, so he is sometimes referred to as the Morning Star of the Reformation.

Answer the questions.

1. What kept John Wycliffe from earning his doctorate until 1372? _____

2. Why did Wycliffe first get into trouble with the Roman Catholic Church? _____

   _____

   _____

3. What are two beliefs that Wycliffe disagreed with the church on? _____

   _____

4. What is Wycliffe credited with writing? _____

5. What is Wycliffe sometimes called? _____

Study Guide

Number in order the events relating to the Battle of Hastings.

_____ William and his army met Harold's force on a field near the town of Hastings.

_____ William asked his vassals to provide him with men and supplies to form an army.

_____ The king of England died in 1066 without an heir.

_____ Harold was killed in the fierce struggle and his army fled soon afterward.

_____ Harold forced William to attack first by placing his men along the top of a hill.

_____ Harold set himself up as the next king.

_____ The Norman army finally broke through.

_____ Two nobles, Harold Godwinson and Duke William of Normandy, both claimed the throne.

_____ William and the Norman army attacked the wall again and again.

_____ William became the king of England.

_____ Harold's men stood side by side with shields raised, forming a wall of shields.

Mark all the correct answers.

12. As a result of the Norman Conquest, ____.

    ○ all England became a feudal kingdom

    ○ William was called William the Conqueror

    ○ a royal line called the Normans began

13. In the legal system in England during the reign of Henry II, ____.

    ○ the courts practiced trial by ordeal

    ○ the king decided all legal matters

    ○ a sheriff decided land ownership with the help of a trial by jury

Answer the questions.

14. Contrast trial by ordeal and trial by jury.

    _____

    _____

    _____

    _____

    _____

    _____

15. Who succeeded Henry II to the throne? Why was he unpopular with the people? _____

    _____

    _____

    _____

Study Guide

Number the events leading to the signing of the Magna Carta.

_____ Negotiations to end the conflict between the nobles and the king included a demand that John sign the Magna Carta.

_____ Nobles examined English laws and determined that King John's abuses of power were violating their rights.

_____ The Magna Carta was confirmed by the king's council and approved by the pope.

_____ The nobles led a revolt against King John.

_____ John signed the Magna Carta.

_____ The nobles agreed that the king's power needed to be limited.

Answer the questions.

22. What was the significance of the Magna Carta? How did it influence later documents? _____

_____

_____

_____

_____

_____

_____

Write _True_ if the statement is true. If the statement is false, write the correction for the underlined words.

_____ 23. Trial by ordeal gave more authority to <u>feudal lords</u>.

_____ 24. The famine and plague <u>strengthened</u> Europe's feudal economy.

_____ 25. The Hundred Years' War weakened feudalism as power shifted from feudal lords to <u>monarchs</u> and common people.

_____ 26. Conflicts between the church and state eventually led to the compromise agreement that allowed the church to appoint its own <u>officials</u>.

_____ 27. The Crusades caused some <u>serfs</u> to sell or mortgage their properties to pay for their Crusade expenses.

_____ 28. The Renaissance brought a rebirth of <u>learning</u>.

_____ 29. Some scholars and thinkers made efforts to return to the teachings and practices of the Scriptures, eventually leading to the <u>Reformation</u>.

A Kingdom from Shore to Shore   _____

Complete the outline as you read about Creation, Fall, and Redemption on pages 318–20.

I. Creation

    A. God created man in His _____ and gave him dominion over the earth.

      1. God created all people with a _____ to do.

      2. As they filled and ruled the earth, people developed _____.

    B. Mankind has exercised _____ over the earth.

      1. _____ harnessed the Nile and built pyramids.

      2. _____ developed roads, cities, and systems of government.

      3. _____ and _____ developed philosophies.

    C. Civilizations are great because humans made in _____ image built them.

      1. Ancient people designed structures, developed _____, and wrote poetry.

      2. Ancient people had a sense of _____ and wrong.

      3. God deserves _____ and _____ for the greatness of civilizations.

II. The Fall

    A. Humans' abilities were _____ by the Fall.

    B. People used the abilities God gave them to _____ against Him.

    C. False religions and philosophies formed because people _____ God's truth.

III. Redemption

    A. When Jesus died, He paid the _____ for sinful people in all times and in all places.

    B. Those who turn from their sin to Christ for salvation receive His _____.

    C. One day, Jesus will rule over the _____ from Jerusalem. He will end all

      _____ and oppression.

Creation and Dominion Organizer

_____

Page 15 of your Student Text says that "people carry out [the Creation Mandate] by using resources and adapting their environment to meet their needs." Fill in the blanks to review some ways the civilizations of the ancient world carried out the Creation Mandate. (The sentences will focus on language, science, technology, and art.)

Chapter 1

1. Tubal-cain forged bronze and iron into useful _____ and instruments. (page 18)

2. Jubal was the father of those who played the _____ and pipe. (page 18)

Chapter 2

1. Sumerian farmers developed the _____ to prepare the soil for planting, the _____ to help oxen pull a plow, and the _____ to allow carts to move easier. (page 24)

2. The Sumerians developed _____ to supply water to crops. (page 26)

Chapter 3

1. Many farmers used a _____ to dip water from the Nile into irrigation canals. (page 51)

2. Egyptians used a _____ to measure the Nile's water levels. (page 54)

3. Egyptians wrote records on _____. (page 56)

Chapter 4

1. One of the Phoenicians' greatest achievements was the development of an _____. (page 84)

2. The temple in Jerusalem was built from huge stones and _____ timbers from the Lebanon Mountains. (page 85)

Chapter 5

1. Harappan artifacts display a language written in _____. (page 103)

2. The Aryans trained _____ to pull lightweight chariots with two wheels. (page 104)

Chapter 6

1. Farmers produced _____ for colorful clothes; artisans made vases and dishes from white _____; the Shang carved statues from _____. (page 122)

2. A _____ could be turned to change a ship's direction. (page 132)

3. The _____ was used to detect earthquakes. (page 132)

Chapter 7

1. Darius built a system of stone _____ to connect the empire. (page 144)

2. The Persians adopted the use of _____ for trade. (page 145)

Creation and Dominion Organizer _____

Chapter 8

1. Archimedes advanced the _____, Euclid wrote the first _____ book, Pythagoras developed a theorem about _____, and Eratosthenes drew lines of _____ and longitude. (page 179)

Chapter 9

1. The Etruscans improved Rome by paving _____, building _____, draining _____, and constructing a _____ system. (page 188)

Chapter 10

1. Mosaics in the Hagia Sophia were made of colored _____, stone, or other materials. (page 220)

2. Cyril and Methodius developed an alphabet for the _____ people. (page 229)

Chapter 11

1. The Olmecs were among the first people to use _____. (page 239)

2. The Aztecs built _____ to connect their islands to the mainland and _____ to separate fresh water from salt water. (page 250)

Chapter 12

1. The Tuareg used camels to travel across the _____; they used camel hides to make _____ and made butter and _____ from camel milk. (page 270)

2. In eastern coastal cities, masons built some houses out of _____. (page 273)

Chapter 13

1. Japanese art used _____ colors and _____ objects. (page 286)

2. Nobles surrounded buildings with elegant gardens and _____. (page 286)

Chapter 14

1. Alcuin developed a new style of writing which used _____ and _____ letters. (page 299)

2. To help with the cold and dark in castles, lords painted the walls and ceilings with _____ colors, placed burning _____ in rooms, put _____ on floors, and hung _____ on walls. (page 312)

Fall and Redemption Organizer

_____

Fill in the blanks to show ways the Fall and Redemption are seen in regions discussed in this chapter.

Egypt

Fall: Egyptians worshiped false gods and treated their _____ as gods. Pharaohs often ruled _____. Egyptians _____ the Israelites. (page 321)

Redemption: The gospel may have been taken to Egypt shortly after Christ's _____. The Egyptian city of _____ was important in early Christianity. (page 324)

Mesopotamia and Persia

Fall: Assyrians were known for fierceness and _____. Babylonian rulers lived _____. Persians introduced the false religion of _____. (page 325)

Redemption: Christ's kingdom spread into Mesopotamia, Persia, and beyond as Christians traveled _____ of the Roman Empire. (page 325)

Greece, Rome, and Europe

Fall: People of Greece and Rome worshiped many different _____ and brought new ideas and _____ to the world. (page 326)

Redemption: The apostle _____ traveled throughout Asia Minor and Greece, sharing the gospel and planting churches. The Protestant _____ tried to restore biblical teaching to the church. (page 326)

India

Fall: Ancient India was the birthplace of two major world religions: _____ and _____. (page 327)

The three main Hindu gods are Brahma, Vishnu, and Shiva. Brahma is believed to have made the world, Vishnu to preserve it by balancing good and evil, and Shiva to destroy it in order to make it better.

Redemption: Tradition says _____ first brought the gospel to India. _____ Christians made contact with Indian Christians by the fourth century. _____ _____ went to India in 1792. (page 327)

Fall and Redemption Organizer

_____

Africa

Fall: Much of ancient Africa was dominated by traditional beliefs involving the _____ world. (page 328)

Redemption: Until the Muslim conquest of the seventh century, Christianity grew in Egypt and other parts of _____ Africa. The building of British and German colonies in Africa opened the way for missionaries like Robert and Mary _____. (page 328)

Latin America

Fall: Mesoamericans had civilizations that practiced human _____. (page 319)

Redemption: When Spanish and Portuguese rule ended, Latin American nations became more open to Protestant _____. Bible societies sent missionaries and distributed _____ in Portuguese, Spanish, and other native languages. (page 330)

China

Fall: When the Tang Dynasty ended, foreign religions in China came under attack, and Christianity was _____. (page 330)

Redemption: _____ _____ was one of the first English missionaries to China. _____ _____ wanted to take the gospel to the interior of China. (pages 330–31)

Robert Morrison and his assistant, William Milne, finished translating the Bible into Chinese in 1819. Their translation, printed on a movable-type printing press, was published in 1823.

Japan

Fall: _____ and Buddhism held sway over the people of Japan. (page 331)

Redemption: An American diplomat who was negotiating a trade agreement with Japan helped open Japan to _____ work. (page 331)

Study Guide

_____

Mark the correct answer.

1. How did persecution help the spread of Christianity?

   ○ Believers carried the gospel with them as they fled to other parts of the world.
   ○ Believers went into hiding and formed underground churches.
   ○ The spread of Christ's kingdom is not consistent in all places and at all times.

2. What is the key to developing a biblical worldview?

   ○ knowing the facts of history
   ○ being familiar with many philosophies and religions
   ○ knowing what God says in His Word

3. Which is an illustration of man's dominion over the earth?

   ○ Siddhartha Gautama developed the religion of Buddhism.
   ○ Hannibal was one of the greatest generals in ancient history.
   ○ The Egyptians and the Mesopotamians used irrigation to water their crops.

4. How did the Fall affect the abilities people have because they are made in God's image?

   ○ The abilities were unchanged.
   ○ The abilities were damaged.
   ○ The abilities were destroyed.

5. Which is _not_ part of God's plan to redeem mankind from sin and its effects in the world?

   ○ Jesus died to pay the penalty for sinful people in all times and in all places.
   ○ One day, Jesus will return to rule over the earth from Jerusalem.
   ○ Philosophers have tackled difficult problems and beliefs.

6. What promise did Jesus give about His kingdom in Matthew 13:33?

   ○ If believers were not faithful, their churches would be removed.
   ○ The kingdom of God would continue to grow gradually.
   ○ The kingdom of God would come suddenly at the end of time.

7. What is the source of the intelligence and sense of justice in people?

   ○ the image of God in man
   ○ the mercy of God in man
   ○ the grace of God in man

8. Why did false religions and philosophies form?

   ○ As bearers of His image, people wanted to use the abilities God gave them.
   ○ People did not know the truth.
   ○ People rejected God's truth.

9. What was surprising about Isaiah's prediction that Egyptians would one day be considered God's people?

   ○ Egypt was very powerful.
   ○ Egyptians worshiped false gods and often acted unjustly.
   ○ Egypt was close to Israel.

10. How did the attitude of Persian rulers toward Christianity change over time?

    ○ The attitude changed from tolerance to persecution.
    ○ The attitude changed from persecution to acceptance.
    ○ The attitude changed from tolerance to embracing Christianity.

Study Guide

Match the description to the correct person.

_____ 1. a missionary to southern Africa

_____ 2. helped start the Protestant Reformation

_____ 3. taught that justification was by faith alone

_____ 4. a missionary to India

_____ 5. trained national pastors and evangelists

_____ 6. set up a mission station and began a church

A Martin Luther   **B** Robert Moffat   **C** William Carey

Answer the questions.

7. Where did Paul share the gospel and plant churches? _____

_____

8. What was the purpose of the Protestant Reformation? _____

_____

9. How did the Reformation in Europe affect the rest of the world? _____

_____

10. What evidence is there of early Christian witness in India? _____

_____

11. Why did Dutch and British trading companies forbid evangelism of Indians by Protestant missionaries?

_____

12. What opened the way for more missionaries in India? _____

_____

13. After Christ's time on earth, what parts of Africa did the gospel quickly spread into? _____

_____

14. What reduced the influence of Christianity in northern Africa? _____

_____

15. What prepared the way for missionaries to go farther south in Africa? _____

_____

16. Whom do African Christians want to provide the leadership of their churches today? _____

_____

Compare-Contrast Essay

_____

Choose a topic to compare and contrast two civilizations with. Use the T-chart to help you take notes on your topic.

Topic: _____

Civilization:	Civilization:

Use the Venn diagram to help you organize the information you have collected.

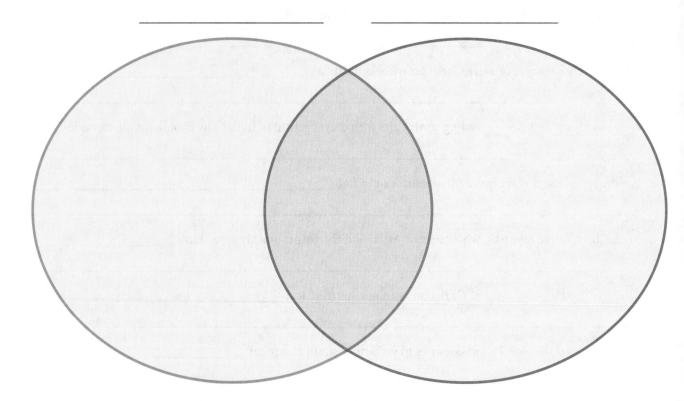

Circle how you will organize your essay.

by similarities and differences

by subject

Complete your essay using the steps on Student Text page 329.

Study Guide

_____

Complete the section.

1. What was happening to the Aztecs as the Protestant Reformation was taking place in Europe in the 1500s?

   _____

2. What religion did the Spaniards bring to Latin America? _____

3. How did missionaries and immigrants help spread the gospel in Latin America? _____

   _____

   _____

   _____

4. What kept Christianity out of China for so long? _____

5. Which missionary to China did not openly evangelize and focused on translation work? _____

   _____

6. Who started the China Inland Mission? _____

7. Why did Hudson Taylor feel that the mission workers needed to support themselves? _____

   _____

8. What was the result of the Boxer Rebellion? _____

   _____

9. Who took over China after World War II and forced the missionaries to leave? _____

   _____

10. What religions held sway over the people of Japan? _____

11. How were missionaries able to enter Japan? _____

   _____

Fill in the blank.

12. Many Christians in China have had to endure _____ and meet in _____.

13. Christianity's spread in Japan has been _____, and Christians are a

    _____ part of the population.

14. The book of Revelation declares that Christ's kingdom will include people of _____ tribe

    and nation.

Study Guide

Write a rough draft of your worldview essay in the space below.

15. Describe your worldview.

_____

_____

_____

_____

_____

_____

_____

_____

_____

_____

_____

_____

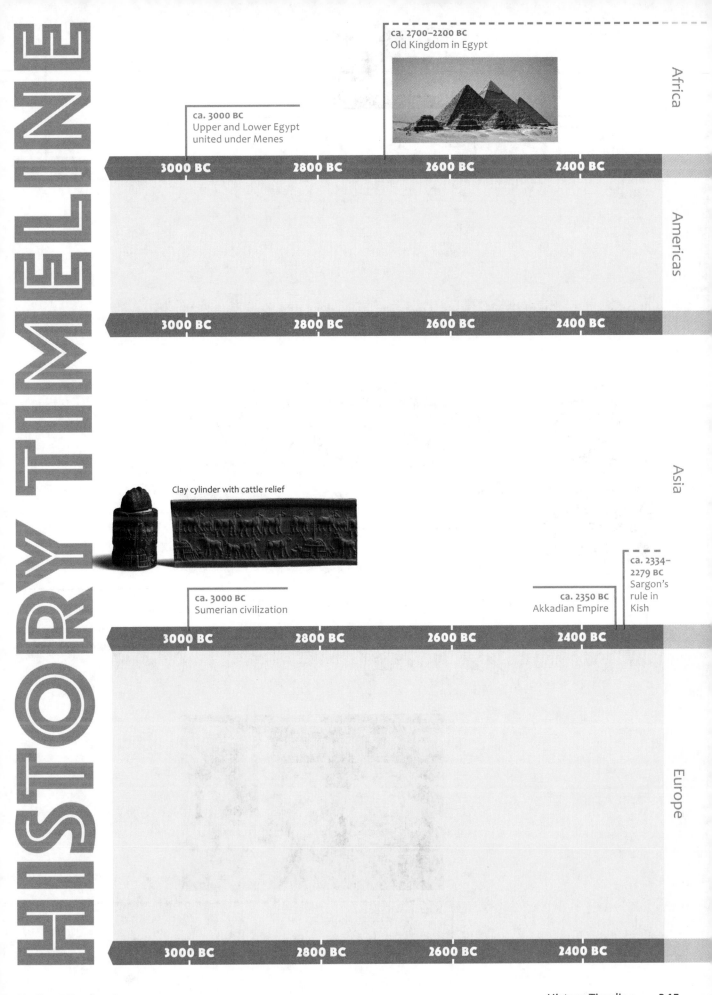

ca. 2700–2200 BC
Old Kingdom in Egypt

Africa

ca. 3000 BC
Upper and Lower Egypt
united under Menes

| 3000 BC | 2800 BC | 2600 BC | 2400 BC |

Americas

| 3000 BC | 2800 BC | 2600 BC | 2400 BC |

Asia

Clay cylinder with cattle relief

ca. 2334–2279 BC
Sargon's
rule in
Kish

ca. 3000 BC
Sumerian civilization

ca. 2350 BC
Akkadian Empire

| 3000 BC | 2800 BC | 2600 BC | 2400 BC |

Europe

| 3000 BC | 2800 BC | 2600 BC | 2400 BC |

Africa

ca. 2700–2200 BC
Old Kingdom in Egypt

ca. 2250 BC
Kushite capital at Kerma

ca. 2040–1650 BC
Middle Kingdom in Egypt

ca. 1570–1075 BC
New Kingdom in Egypt

Black Pyramid

| 2200 BC | 2000 BC | 1800 BC | 1700 BC | 1600 BC |

Americas

| 2200 BC | 2000 BC | 1800 BC | 1700 BC | 1600 BC |

Asia

Harappan artifact

Ziggurat of Ur

ca. 2091 BC
God instructs Abram to leave Haran

ca. 2050 BC
Beginning of Ur-Nammu's rule in Sumer

ca. 2000 BC
Hittite settlement in Asia Minor

1700–1500 BC
Disappearance of Harappan civilization

ca. 2300 BC
Harappan civilization

| 2200 BC | 2000 BC | 1800 BC | 1700 BC | 1600 BC |

Europe

Minoan pottery

ca. 2000–1400 BC
Minoan civilization in Greece

| 2200 BC | 2000 BC | 1800 BC | 1700 BC | 1600 BC |

Africa

ca. 1570–1075 BC
New Kingdom in Egypt

Burial mask
of King
Tutankhamun

1500 BC
Kush conquered
by Egypt

1446 BC
Exodus from
Egypt

ca. 1330 BC
Beginning of King
Tutankhamun's
rule in Egypt

1500 BC **1400 BC** **1300 BC** **1200 BC**

Americas

ca. 1200–400 BC
Olmec
civilization

1500 BC **1400 BC** **1300 BC** **1200 BC**

Asia

ca. 1500–1000 BC
Shang dynasty in China

Shang
dynasty
ting

Moses given
the Law by God

ca. 1500 BC
Rig-Veda (India)

ca. 1500 BC
Aryan civilization
in India

ca. 1440 BC
First book of the Pentateuch
written by Moses

1500 BC **1400 BC** **1300 BC** **1200 BC**

Europe

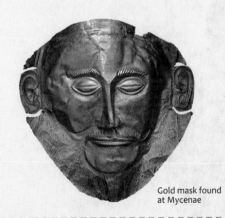

Gold mask found
at Mycenae

Homer

ca. 1200 BC
Life of Homer,
Greek poet
and storyteller

ca. 1400–1200 BC
Mycenaean civilization in Greece

1500 BC **1400 BC** **1300 BC** **1200 BC**

ca. 1570–1075 BC
New Kingdom in Egypt

Kushite
temple

ca. 1000 BC
Egypt conquered
by Kush

1100 BC	1000 BC	900 BC	800 BC

Americas

Giant
stone
head

ca. 1200–400 BC
Olmec
civilization

1100 BC	1000 BC	900 BC	800 BC

Asia

ca. 1500–1000 BC
Shang dynasty in China

ca. 1000–221 BC
Zhou dynasty in China

King Wu of the
Zhou dynasty

ca. 1000 BC
Chaldean settlement
around Babylon

969 BC
Death of Israelite king David;
beginning of Solomon's rule

932 BC
Death of King Solomon; beginning of
Rehoboam's rule; Israel divided in two

1020 BC
Saul anointed as
Israelite king

1100 BC	1000 BC	900 BC	800 BC

Europe

1150–750 BC
Grecian dark age

Spartan
warriors

753 BC
Legendary founding of Rome
by Romulus and Remus

1100 BC	1000 BC	900 BC	800 BC

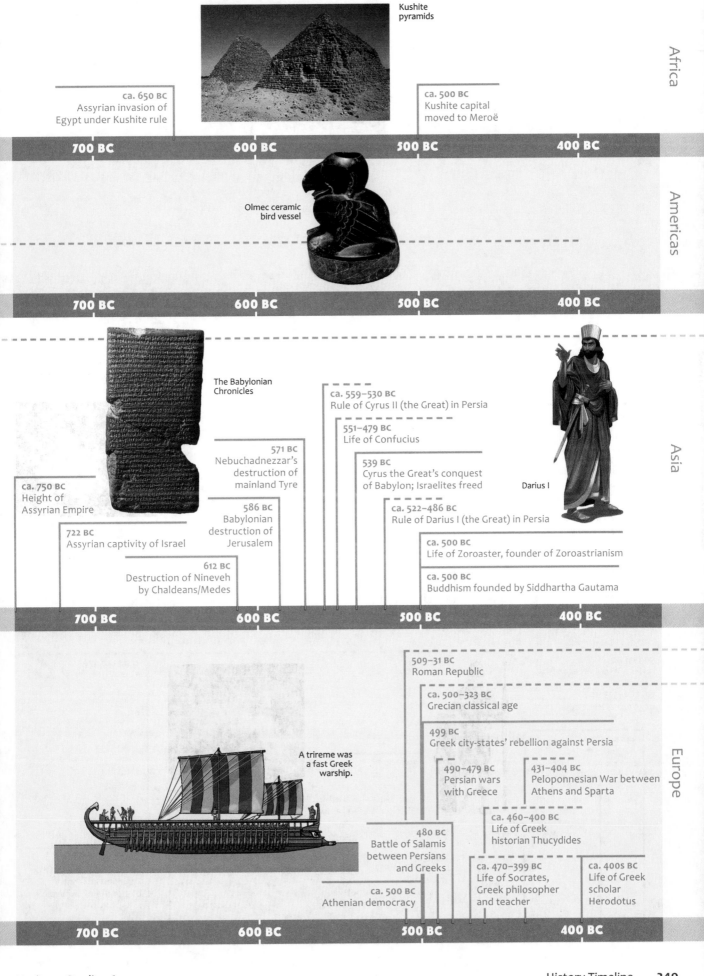

Africa

Kushite pyramids

ca. 650 BC
Assyrian invasion of Egypt under Kushite rule

ca. 500 BC
Kushite capital moved to Meroë

700 BC | 600 BC | 500 BC | 400 BC

Americas

Olmec ceramic bird vessel

700 BC | 600 BC | 500 BC | 400 BC

Asia

The Babylonian Chronicles

ca. 559–530 BC
Rule of Cyrus II (the Great) in Persia

551–479 BC
Life of Confucius

571 BC
Nebuchadnezzar's destruction of mainland Tyre

539 BC
Cyrus the Great's conquest of Babylon; Israelites freed

Darius I

ca. 750 BC
Height of Assyrian Empire

586 BC
Babylonian destruction of Jerusalem

ca. 522–486 BC
Rule of Darius I (the Great) in Persia

722 BC
Assyrian captivity of Israel

ca. 500 BC
Life of Zoroaster, founder of Zoroastrianism

612 BC
Destruction of Nineveh by Chaldeans/Medes

ca. 500 BC
Buddhism founded by Siddhartha Gautama

700 BC | 600 BC | 500 BC | 400 BC

Europe

509–31 BC
Roman Republic

ca. 500–323 BC
Grecian classical age

499 BC
Greek city-states' rebellion against Persia

A trireme was a fast Greek warship.

490–479 BC
Persian wars with Greece

431–404 BC
Peloponnesian War between Athens and Sparta

ca. 460–400 BC
Life of Greek historian Thucydides

480 BC
Battle of Salamis between Persians and Greeks

ca. 470–399 BC
Life of Socrates, Greek philosopher and teacher

ca. 400s BC
Life of Greek scholar Herodotus

ca. 500 BC
Athenian democracy

700 BC | 600 BC | 500 BC | 400 BC

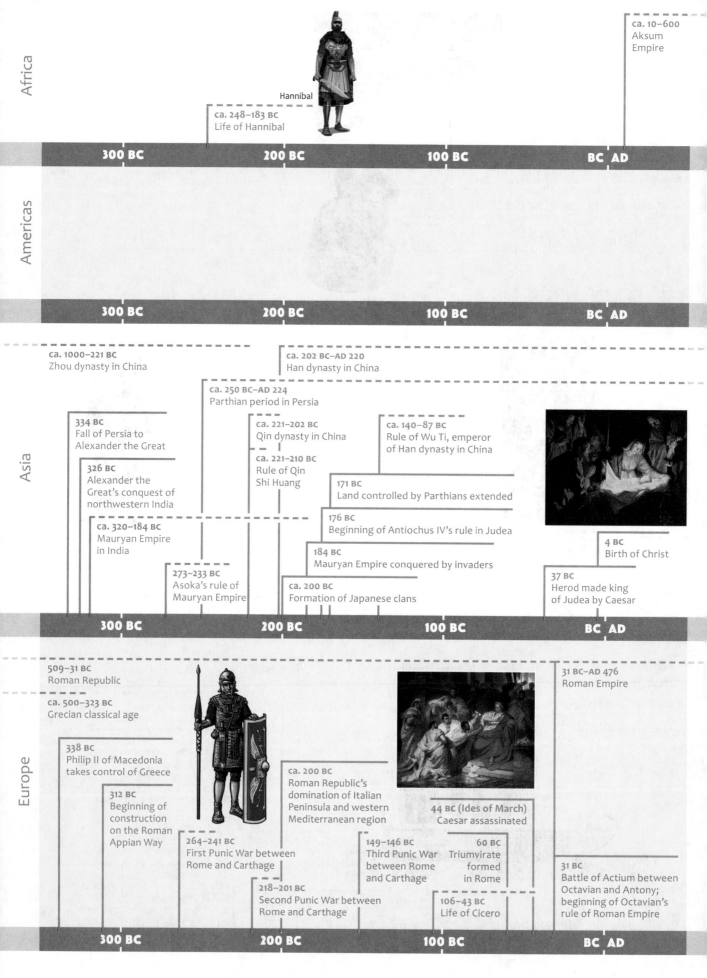

Africa

ca. 10–600
Aksum
Empire

Hannibal

ca. 248–183 BC
Life of Hannibal

| 300 BC | 200 BC | 100 BC | BC AD |

Americas

| 300 BC | 200 BC | 100 BC | BC AD |

Asia

ca. 1000–221 BC
Zhou dynasty in China

ca. 202 BC–AD 220
Han dynasty in China

ca. 250 BC–AD 224
Parthian period in Persia

334 BC
Fall of Persia to
Alexander the Great

ca. 221–202 BC
Qin dynasty in China

ca. 140–87 BC
Rule of Wu Ti, emperor
of Han dynasty in China

326 BC
Alexander the
Great's conquest of
northwestern India

ca. 221–210 BC
Rule of Qin
Shi Huang

171 BC
Land controlled by Parthians extended

ca. 320–184 BC
Mauryan Empire
in India

176 BC
Beginning of Antiochus IV's rule in Judea

184 BC
Mauryan Empire conquered by invaders

4 BC
Birth of Christ

273–233 BC
Asoka's rule of
Mauryan Empire

ca. 200 BC
Formation of Japanese clans

37 BC
Herod made king
of Judea by Caesar

| 300 BC | 200 BC | 100 BC | BC AD |

Europe

509–31 BC
Roman Republic

31 BC–AD 476
Roman Empire

ca. 500–323 BC
Grecian classical age

338 BC
Philip II of Macedonia
takes control of Greece

ca. 200 BC
Roman Republic's
domination of Italian
Peninsula and western
Mediterranean region

44 BC (Ides of March)
Caesar assassinated

312 BC
Beginning of
construction
on the Roman
Appian Way

264–241 BC
First Punic War between
Rome and Carthage

149–146 BC
Third Punic War
between Rome
and Carthage

60 BC
Triumvirate
formed
in Rome

218–201 BC
Second Punic War between
Rome and Carthage

106–43 BC
Life of Cicero

31 BC
Battle of Actium between
Octavian and Antony;
beginning of Octavian's
rule of Roman Empire

| 300 BC | 200 BC | 100 BC | BC AD |

Africa

King Ezana

ca. 300s
King Ezana's rule in Aksum

330
Kush conquered by Aksum

| AD 100 | AD 200 | AD 300 | AD 400 |

Americas

ca. 250–900
Mayan civilization

| AD 100 | AD 200 | AD 300 | AD 400 |

Asia

ca. 250–700
Yamato clan in Japan

ca. 224-651
Sassanid period in Persia

Romans carrying spoils from the Jerusalem temple

70
Roman destruction of Jerusalem and temple; end of Israelite nation

72
Fall of two Jewish strongholds to Romans

ca. 400
Beginning of Golden Age of India

| AD 100 | AD 200 | AD 300 | AD 400 |

Europe

Roman Colosseum

284–305
Diocletian's rule of Roman Empire

306–337
Rule of Roman emperor Constantine

313
Edict of Milan

325
Council of Nicaea

330
Roman capital moved to Constantinople

378
Battle of Adrianople between Romans and Visigoths

395
Roman Empire divided by Theodosius I

69
Civil war in Roman Empire

180
End of Pax Romana

| AD 100 | AD 200 | AD 300 | AD 400 |

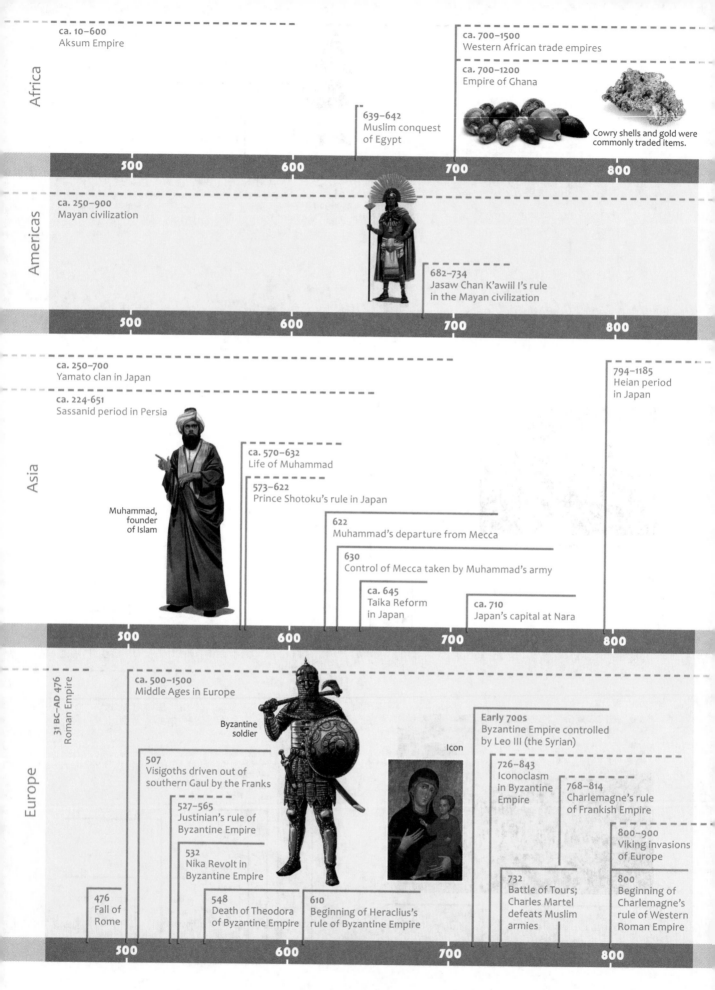

Africa

ca. 10–600
Aksum Empire

ca. 700–1500
Western African trade empires

ca. 700–1200
Empire of Ghana

639–642
Muslim conquest
of Egypt

Cowry shells and gold were
commonly traded items.

500   600   700   800

Americas

ca. 250–900
Mayan civilization

682–734
Jasaw Chan K'awiil I's rule
in the Mayan civilization

500   600   700   800

Asia

ca. 250–700
Yamato clan in Japan

ca. 224-651
Sassanid period in Persia

794–1185
Heian period
in Japan

ca. 570–632
Life of Muhammad

573–622
Prince Shotoku's rule in Japan

622
Muhammad's departure from Mecca

Muhammad,
founder
of Islam

630
Control of Mecca taken by Muhammad's army

ca. 645
Taika Reform
in Japan

ca. 710
Japan's capital at Nara

500   600   700   800

Europe

ca. 500–1500
Middle Ages in Europe

31 BC–AD 476
Roman Empire

Byzantine
soldier

Early 700s
Byzantine Empire controlled
by Leo III (the Syrian)

Icon

507
Visigoths driven out of
southern Gaul by the Franks

726–843
Iconoclasm
in Byzantine
Empire

768–814
Charlemagne's rule
of Frankish Empire

527–565
Justinian's rule of
Byzantine Empire

532
Nika Revolt in
Byzantine Empire

800–900
Viking invasions
of Europe

476
Fall of
Rome

548
Death of Theodora
of Byzantine Empire

610
Beginning of Heraclius's
rule of Byzantine Empire

732
Battle of Tours;
Charles Martel
defeats Muslim
armies

800
Beginning of
Charlemagne's
rule of Western
Roman Empire

500   600   700   800

ca. 900s
Coastal trade
cities established
in eastern Africa

Rhinoceros horns
and ivory from
elephant tusks
were traded in
eastern Africa.

ca. 1200
Beginning of
Sundiata's
rule in Mali

900   1000   1100   1200

ca. 869
Mayas' sudden
exit from cities

900   1000   1100   1200

Heian Palace

1187
Jerusalem recaptured
from crusaders by
Muslims

1192
Yoritomo
appointed as
the first shogun

1096–1099
First Crusade

1099
European crusaders'
capture of Jerusalem
from Muslims

ca. 1200
Middle East from
Egypt to Syria
under control of
Muslim Turks

900   1000   1100   1200

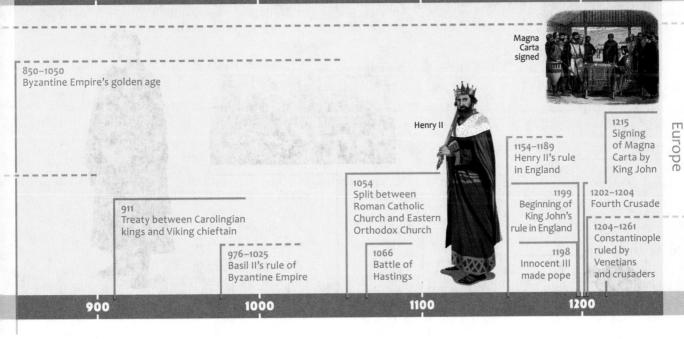

Magna
Carta
signed

850–1050
Byzantine Empire's golden age

Henry II

1154–1189
Henry II's rule
in England

1215
Signing
of Magna
Carta by
King John

911
Treaty between Carolingian
kings and Viking chieftain

1054
Split between
Roman Catholic
Church and Eastern
Orthodox Church

1199
Beginning of
King John's
rule in England

1202–1204
Fourth Crusade

976–1025
Basil II's rule of
Byzantine Empire

1066
Battle of
Hastings

1198
Innocent III
made pope

1204–1261
Constantinople
ruled by
Venetians
and crusaders

900   1000   1100   1200

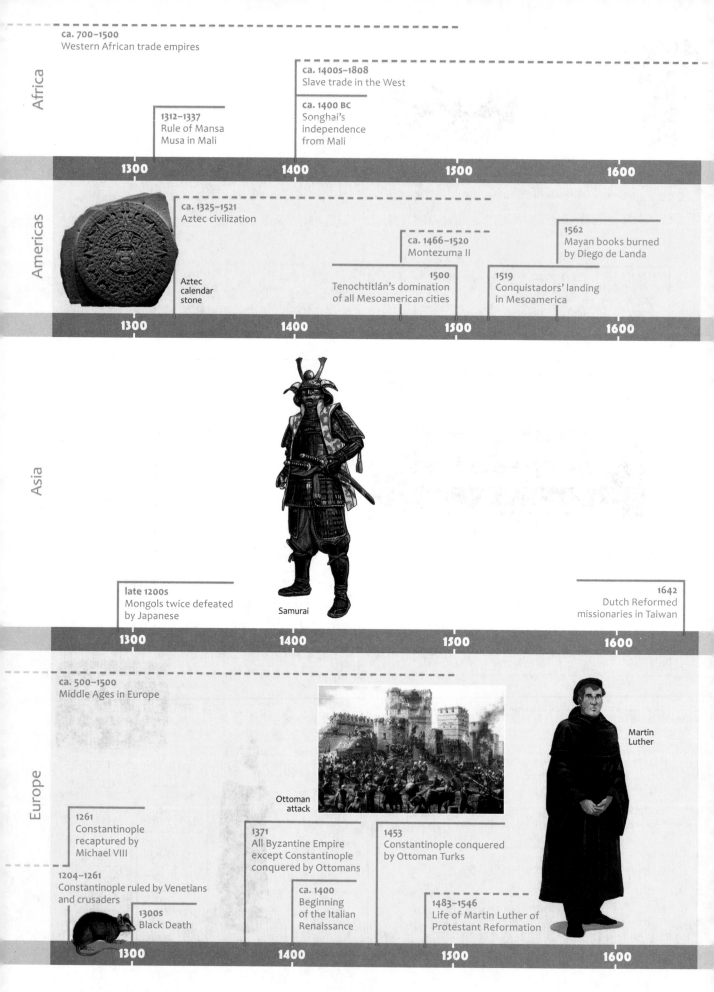

Africa

ca. 700–1500
Western African trade empires

ca. 1400s–1808
Slave trade in the West

ca. 1400 BC
Songhai's
independence
from Mali

1312–1337
Rule of Mansa
Musa in Mali

| 1300 | 1400 | 1500 | 1600 |

Americas

ca. 1325–1521
Aztec civilization

1562
Mayan books burned
by Diego de Landa

ca. 1466–1520
Montezuma II

Aztec
calendar
stone

1500
Tenochtitlán's domination
of all Mesoamerican cities

1519
Conquistadors' landing
in Mesoamerica

| 1300 | 1400 | 1500 | 1600 |

Asia

Samurai

late 1200s
Mongols twice defeated
by Japanese

1642
Dutch Reformed
missionaries in Taiwan

| 1300 | 1400 | 1500 | 1600 |

Europe

ca. 500–1500
Middle Ages in Europe

Ottoman
attack

Martin
Luther

1261
Constantinople
recaptured by
Michael VIII

1371
All Byzantine Empire
except Constantinople
conquered by Ottomans

1453
Constantinople conquered
by Ottoman Turks

1204–1261
Constantinople ruled by Venetians
and crusaders

ca. 1400
Beginning
of the Italian
Renaissance

1483–1546
Life of Martin Luther of
Protestant Reformation

1300s
Black Death

| 1300 | 1400 | 1500 | 1600 |

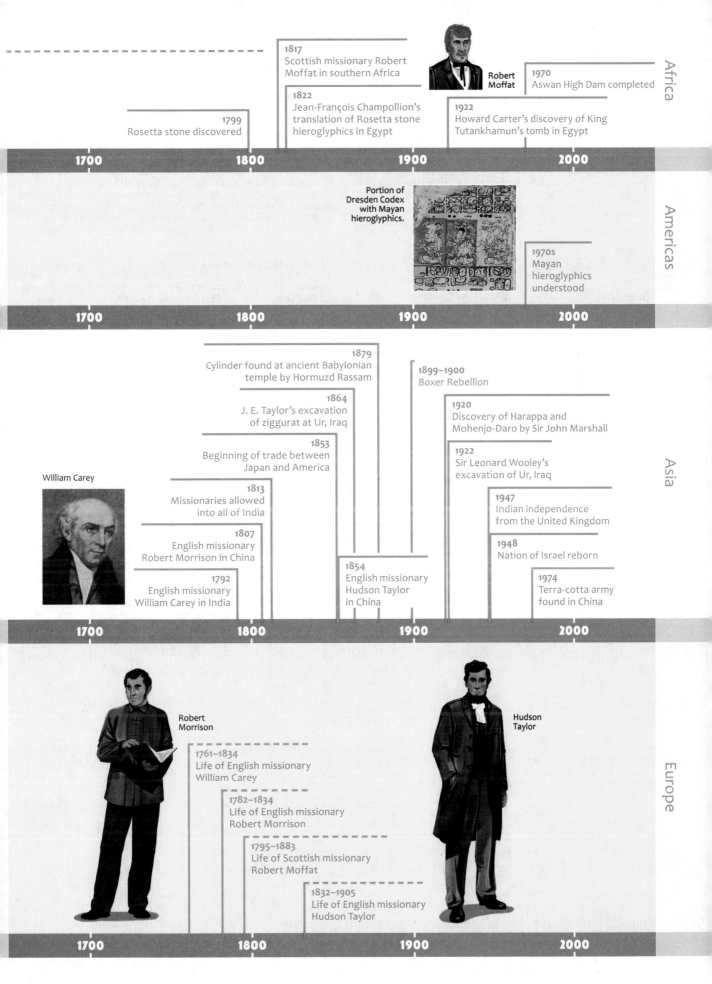

Africa

1817
Scottish missionary Robert Moffat in southern Africa

Robert Moffat

1970
Aswan High Dam completed

1822
Jean-François Champollion's translation of Rosetta stone hieroglyphics in Egypt

1799
Rosetta stone discovered

1922
Howard Carter's discovery of King Tutankhamun's tomb in Egypt

1700   1800   1900   2000

Americas

Portion of Dresden Codex with Mayan hieroglyphics.

1970s
Mayan hieroglyphics understood

1700   1800   1900   2000

Asia

1879
Cylinder found at ancient Babylonian temple by Hormuzd Rassam

1899–1900
Boxer Rebellion

1864
J. E. Taylor's excavation of ziggurat at Ur, Iraq

1920
Discovery of Harappa and Mohenjo-Daro by Sir John Marshall

1853
Beginning of trade between Japan and America

1922
Sir Leonard Wooley's excavation of Ur, Iraq

William Carey

1813
Missionaries allowed into all of India

1947
Indian independence from the United Kingdom

1807
English missionary Robert Morrison in China

1948
Nation of Israel reborn

1792
English missionary William Carey in India

1854
English missionary Hudson Taylor in China

1974
Terra-cotta army found in China

1700   1800   1900   2000

Europe

Robert Morrison

1761–1834
Life of English missionary William Carey

Hudson Taylor

1782–1834
Life of English missionary Robert Morrison

1795–1883
Life of Scottish missionary Robert Moffat

1832–1905
Life of English missionary Hudson Taylor

1700   1800   1900   2000

PHOTO CREDITS

Key:
(t) top; (c) center; (b) bottom;
(l) left; (r) right

Chapter 1

2 Photos.com/Thinkstock; **4** "Among the Sierra Nevada Mountains, California" by Albert Bierstadt; **5** sumikophoto/Shutterstock.com; **7** © iStockphoto.com/Floriano Rescigno

Chapter 2

21 Werner Forman/Universal Images Group/Getty Images; **22** Granger, NYC

Chapter 3

35 Jochen Schlenker/MediaBakery; **49** DEA/G. DAGLI ORTI/De Agostini/Getty Images

Chapter 6

91 fuyu liu/Shutterstock.com; **93** "Lidded Ritual Food Cauldron (Ding) with Interlaced Dragons LACMA M.74.103a-b (2 of 5)"/LACMA/Wikimedia Commons /Public Domain

Chapter 9

144 Oronoz/Album/SuperStock; **146** Nicholas Pitt / Alamy Stock Photo; **149** DEA PICTURE LIBRARY/Getty Images; **151** www.BibleLandPictures.com / Alamy Stock Photo

Chapter 10

157 iSailorr/iStock/Thinkstock

Chapter 11

171 The Metropolitan Museum of Art/The Michael C. Rockefeller Memorial Collection, Gift of Nelson A. Rockefeller, 1963, www.metmuseum.org; **175** Purchased with funds provided by Camilla Chandler Frost through the 2008 Collectors Committee (M.2008.59)/www.lacma.org/Public Domain; **176** The Metropolitan Museum of Art/The Purchase, Gift of Elizabeth M. Riley, by exchange, 2000, www.metmuseum.org; **177** rchphoto/Bigstock.com; **181** The Metropolitan Museum of Art/Museum Purchase, 1900, www.metmuseum.org

Chapter 12

189 ©iStockphoto.com/assalve; **190** ©iStockphoto.com/assalve; **195**t Bjoern Wylezich/Shutterstock.com; **195**tc AlenKadr/Shutterstock.com; **195**bc © Björn Wylezich | Dreamstime.com; **195**b AmyLv/Shutterstock.com; **198** © Reinhardt | Dreamstime.com

Chapter 14

213 vvoevale/Blgstock.com; **215, 220** DeAgostini/SuperStock; **218** DEA/J. E. BULLOZ/DeAgostini Picture Library/Getty Images; **219** Prisma/Album /SuperStock; **224** © 2009 JupiterImages Corporation; **230** "Baldwin of Boulogne entering Edessa in February 1098" by J. Robert-Fleury/Wikimedia Commons /Public Domain; **231** "Richental Konzilssitzung Muenster"/Wikimedia Commons /Public Domain; **232** Heinz-Dieter Falkenstein/age fotostock/SuperStock

Chapter 15

238 "The Hindu Gods Vishnu, Shiva, and Brahma LACMA M.86.337 (1 of 12)" /Wikimedia Commons/Public Domain; **239** © iStock.com/trigga; **241**l "Porträt des Martin Luther" by Lucas Cranach the Elder/Wikimedia Commons/Public Domain; **241**c "George Baxter, The Reverend Robert Moffat, 1 April 1843"/Wikimedia Commons/Public Domain; **241**r William Carey (colour litho), English School, (19th century) / Private Collection / © Look and Learn / Elgar Collection / Bridgeman Images

Timeline

245t "All Gizah Pyramids" by Ricardo Liberato/Wikimedia Commons/CC By-SA 3.0; **245**b, **246**t **247**t DeAgostini/SuperStock; **246**cl 'Priest King' from Mohenjo-Daro, c.2500 BC (steatite), Harappan / National Museum of Karachi, Karachi, Pakistan / Photo © Luca Tettoni / Bridgeman Images; **246**cr Universal History Archive /Universal Images Group/Getty Images; **246**b Getty Images/iStockphoto /Thinkstock; **247**cl "Liu Ding" by Mountain/Wikimedia Commons/CC By-SA 3.0; **247**b "Funeral mask of Agamemnon-colorcorr" by DieBuche/Wikimedia Commons/CC By-SA 3.0; **248**t Ignatius Tan/Shutterstock.com; **248**cl © iStock.com /arturogi; **248**cr CPA Media - Pictures from History /Granger, NYC; **249**t De Agostini Picture Library/Getty Images; **249**cl www.BibleLandPictures.com / Alamy Stock Photo; **249**cc The Metropolitan Museum of Art, Rogers Fund, 1986, www.metmuseum.org; **250**t "The Adoration of the Shepherds" by Gerard van Honthorst/Wikimedia Commons/Public Domain; **250**b "Murder of Caesar" by Karl Theodor von Piloty/Wikimedia Commons/Public Domain; **251**t Danita Delimont /Gallo Images/Getty Images; **251**b © Luzav10 | Dreamstime; **252**tl © iStock. com/busypix; **252**tr Bjoern Wylezich/Shutterstock.com; **252**b The Metropolitan Museum of Art, Gift of Irma N. Straus, 1960, www.metmuseum.org; **253**tl © iStock .com/DaveThomasNZ; **253**tr Volodymyr Burdiak/Shutterstock.com; **253**c coward_lion/Bigstock.com; **253**b "A Chronicle of England - Page 226 - John Signs the Great Charter" by James William Edmund Doyle/Wikimedia Commons/Public Domain; **254**t "Monolito de la Piedra del Sol" by El Comandante/ Wikimedia Commons /CC By-SA 3.0; **254**bl Photos.com/Thinkstock; **254**br Lestertair/Shutterstock.com; **255**t "Dresden Codex p09"/Wikimedia Commons/Public Domain; **255**b William Carey (colour litho), English School, (19th century) / Private Collection / © Look and Learn / Elgar Collection / Bridgeman Images